WILD FLOWERS IN COLOUR

WILD FLOWERS
IN COLOUR

*

ILLUSTRATED BY
E. HAHNEWALD

WITH DESCRIPTIONS BY
J. HUTCHINSON

*

PENGUIN BOOKS

Penguin Books Ltd, Harmondsworth, Middlesex, England
Penguin Books Inc., 7110 Ambassador Road, Baltimore, Maryland 21207, U.S.A.
Penguin Books Australia Ltd, Ringwood, Victoria, Australia
Penguin Books Canada Ltd, 41 Steelcase Road West,
Markham, Ontario, Canada
Penguin Books (N.Z.) Ltd, 182-190 Wairau Road,
Auckland 10, New Zealand

—

First published 1958
Reissued 1974

—

Illustrations copyright © E. Hahnewald, 1958
Text copyright © J. Hutchinson, 1958

Made and printed in Great Britain
by Hazell Watson & Viney Ltd,
Aylesbury, Bucks

CONTENTS

FOREWORD

THE coloured pictures of wild flowers in this book were drawn by a Swedish artist, E. Hahnewald, and were originally published in Sweden under the title Floran i Färg. They were accompanied by very short descriptions, mainly relating to habitat and times of flowering, by Lorentz Bolin and Lennart O. A. von Post. Later the same illustrations were used in a Danish edition entitled Flora i Farver.

Owing to differences between the flora of Scandinavia and Britain, it has been necessary to replace some of the original subjects by British species. New illustrations for these have been supplied by the artist.

Owing to their brevity in both the Swedish and Danish editions, and to render the book more useful to British readers, new and fuller descriptions have been included.

CLASSIFICATION

ABOUT eighteen hundred *species* of flowering plants grow wild or have become naturalized in the British Isles. They therefore represent but a fraction (not more than about 1/110) of the whole flora of the world, which is composed of over two hundred thousand species. These species are classified into some fifteen thousand *genera*, and they in turn are arranged in upwards of three hundred *families*. Both genera and families vary greatly in size. A few families contain only one genus, whilst some, such as the Daisy family (*Compositae*), are represented by over a thousand genera.

The classification of flowering plants has exercised the minds of botanists for a very long period. The earliest writers arranged them into Trees, Shrubs and Herbs, thus placing undue emphasis on their habit or mode of growth. Little notice was taken of their flowers and fruits. This simple division prevailed until as late as the eighteenth century.

The English botanist, John Ray (1686–1704), was the first to divide flowering plants into two main groups, which are still maintained, namely *Dicotyledons* (seedlings with two leaves), and *Monocotyledons* (seedlings with one primary seed leaf). After that, however, great progress was made towards a more natural classification, beginning with *herbals*, which were mostly concerned, however, with the economic uses of plants.

Carl Linnaeus, the great Swedish naturalist, early in the eighteenth century, published the first system which brought many related plants together. Linnaeus distinguished his main groups largely by characters derived from the flowers, especially by the number of stamens. For example his group *Pentandria* had five stamens, his *Hexandria* six stamens, and so on. The Wallflower family was called *Tetradynamia*, having six stamens, four of which were long and two shorter. Until Linnaeus' time a descriptive phrase of several words was used to distinguish a species. The common Daisy was called 'Bellis perennis, foliis spathulatis, capitulis multifloris'. He reduced this to *Bellis perennis*. Again the field Buttercup was called 'Ranunculus calycibus retroflexis, pedunculis sulcatis, caule erecto, foliis compositis', and became *Ranunculus bulbosus*.

Eventually more natural systems were invented, by the Jussieus in France, the de Candolles in Switzerland, by Bentham and Hooker in Britain, and by Engler and others in Germany, and many others of minor importance. Even the last of these systems, that of Engler, paid little attention to the Darwinian theory of evolution, and botanists on the whole have been slow to follow the example of geologists and zoologists in modifying their systems accordingly.

The present writer has given a full account of the development of a more natural system in his *Families of Flowering Plants* (1926, 1934), and *The Story of Plants* (with R. Melville) (1948), which may be consulted at many public libraries. There is not space here for more than to point out that the coloured plates and descriptions (with a few exceptions) are arranged in a natural or phylogenetic sequence beginning with the apparently more *primitive* families such as the Cone-bearing plants (*Pinaceae*), the Rose family (*Rosaceae*) and Buttercup family (*Ranunculaceae*), ending with the Daisy family (*Compositae*), and the Deadnettle family (*Labiatae*) amongst the *Dicotyledons*, and with the Orchids (*Orchidaceae*) and Grasses (*Gramineae*) in the *Monocotyledons*. An index to the families represented is given on page 127.

1. Scots Pine, *Pinus sylvestris*   3. Juniper, *Juniperus communis*
2. Norway Spruce, *Picea abies*   4. Yew, *Taxus baccata*

1. Intermediate White Beam, *Sorbus intermedia*
2. Rowan, Mountain Ash, *Sorbus aucuparia*

1. Crab Apple, *Malus pumila*
2. Hawthorn, May, *Crataegus oxyacanthoides*
3. Sloe, *Prunus spinosa*

1. Wild Cherry, Gean, *Prunus avium*
2. Bird Cherry, Heckberry, *Padus racemosa*

1. Meadowsweet, *Filipendula ulmaria*
2. Dropwort, *Filipendula vulgaris*
3. Agrimony, *Agrimonia eupatoria*
4. Common Avens, Herb Bennett, *Geum urbanum*

1. Water Avens, *Geum rivale*
2. Lady's Mantle, *Alchemilla vulgaris*
3. Alpine Lady's Mantle, *Alchemilla alpina*
4. Sibbald's Potentilla, *Potentilla sibbaldii*
5. Mountain Avens, *Dryas octopetala*

1. Shrubby Cinquefoil, *Potentilla fruticosa*
2. Silvery-leaved Cinquefoil, *Potentilla argentea*
3. Spring Cinquefoil, *Potentilla verna*
4. Erect Potentilla, *Potentilla erecta*

7

1. Creeping Cinquefoil, *Potentilla reptans*
2. Silver Weed, *Potentilla anserina*
3. Marsh Cinquefoil, *Potentilla palustris*
4. Wild Strawberry, *Fragaria vesca*

1. Stone Blackberry, *Rubus saxatilis*
2. Cloudberry, *Rubus chamaemorus*
3. Arctic Blackberry, *Rubus arcticus*
4. Dewberry, *Rubus caesius*

9

1. Raspberry, *Rubus idaeus*
2. Blackberry, *Rubus fruticosus*
3. Dog Rose, *Rosa canina*

10

1. Small-leaved Lime, *Tilia cordata*
2. Mountain Ribes, *Ribes alpinum*
3. Entire-leaved Cotoneaster, *Cotoneaster integerrimus*

11

1. Sea Pea, *Lathyrus japonicus*
2. Meadow Pea, *Lathyrus pratensis*
3. Tuberous Pea, *Lathyrus montanus*
4. Tufted Vetch, *Vicia cracca*
5. Bush or Hedge Vetch, *Vicia sepium*

1. Milk Vetch, *Astragalus glycyphyllus*
2. Alpine Astragalus, *Astragalus alpinus*
3. Yellow Oxytropis, *Oxytropis campestris*
4. Bird's-foot Trefoil, *Lotus corniculatus*

13

1. Melilot, *Melilotus altissima*
2. Lucerne, *Medicago sativa*
3. Sickle Medick, *Medicago falcata*
4. Black Medick, *Medicago lupulina*
5. Hop Clover, *Trifolium procumbens*

14

1. Golden Clover, *Trifolium aureum*
2. Crown Vetch, *Coronilla varia*
3. Strawberry Clover, *Trifolium fragiferum*
4. Hare's-foot Trefoil or Clover,
   Trifolium arvense

15

1. Red Clover, *Trifolium pratense*
2. White or Dutch Clover,
   Trifolium repens
3. Alsike Clover, *Trifolium hybridum*
4. Zigzag or Meadow Clover,
   Trifolium medium

1. Rest-Harrow, *Ononis repens*
2. Hairy Genista, *Genista pilosa*
3. Petty Whin, Needle Furze, *Genista anglica*
4. Broom, *Cytisus scoparius*
5. Kidney Vetch, Lady's Fingers, *Anthyllis vulneraria*

17

1. Ivy, *Hedera helix*
2. Dwarf Cornel, *Chamaepericlymenum suecicum*
3. Dogwood, *Cornus sanguinea*

1. Norway Maple, *Acer platanoides*
2. Spindle Tree, *Euonymus europaeus*
3. Alder Buckthorn, Black Alder, *Frangula alnus*
4. Buckthorn, *Rhamnus catharticus*

19

1. Bay Willow, *Salix pentandra*
2. Crack Willow, *Salix fragilis*
3. Osier, *Salix viminalis*
4. Great Sallow Willow, *Salix caprea*

1. Woolly Willow, *Salix lanata*   3. Dwarf Willow, *Salix herbacea*
2. Creeping Willow, *Salix repens*   4. Reticulate Willow, *Salix reticulata*

1. Alder, *Alnus glutinosa*
2. Grey Alder, *Alnus incana*

1. Dwarf Birch, *Betula nana*
2. Bog Myrtle, *Myrica gale*
3. Aspen, *Populus tremula*

23

1. Wych Elm, *Ulmus glabra*
2. Birch, *Betula verrucosa*
3. Birch, *Betula pubescens*

24

1. Hornbeam, *Carpinus betulus*
2. Hazel Nut, *Corylus avellana*

25

1. Beech, *Fagus sylvatica*
2. Pedunculate Oak, *Quercus robur*

1. Sun Spurge, *Euphorbia helioscopia*
2. Dog's Mercury, *Mercurialis perennis*
3. Stinging Nettle, *Urtica dioica*

4. Small Stinging Nettle, *Urtica urens*
5. Hop, *Humulus lupulus*

1. Creeping St John's Wort,
   Hypericum humifusum
2. Marsh Violet, *Viola palustris*

3. Sundew, *Drosera rotundifolia*
4. Rock Rose, *Helianthemum chamaecistus*

28

1. Imperforate St John's Wort,
   Hypericum dubium
2. Upright St John's Wort,
   Hypericum pulchrum
3. Mallow, *Malva sylvestris*
4. Dwarf Mallow, *Malva neglecta*

1. Sweet Violet, *Viola odorata*   3. Wood Violet, *Viola riviniana*
2. Hairy Violet, *Viola hirta*   4. Dog Violet, *Viola canina*

1. Shepherd's Purse, *Capsella bursa-pastoris*
2. Scurvy Grass, *Cochlearia officinalis*
3. Whitlow Grass, *Erophila verna*
4. Heartsease, *Viola tricolor*
5. Field Pansy, *Viola arvensis*

31

1. Small Alison, *Alyssum alyssoides*
2. Hoary Berteroa, *Berteroa incana*
3. Field Penny Cress, *Thlaspi arvense*
4. Alpine Penny Cress, *Thlaspi alpestre*
5. Narrow-leaved Cress, *Lepidium ruderale*

1. Alpine Rockcress, *Arabis alpina*   3. Wall Cress, *Arabidopsis thaliana*
2. Sea Kale, *Crambe maritima*   4. Tower Mustard, *Turritis glabra*

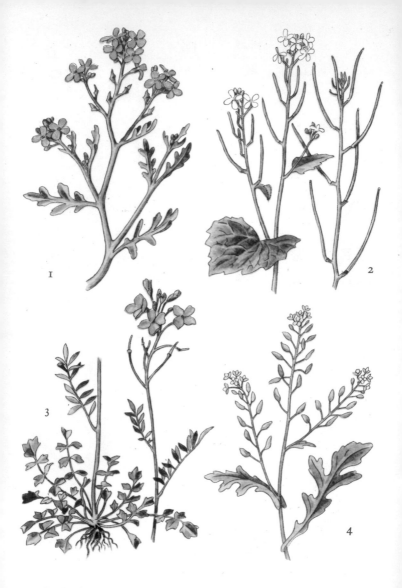

1. Sea Rocket, *Cakile maritima*
2. Garlic Mustard, *Alliaria officinalis*
3. Cuckoo Flower, Lady's Smock,
   Cardamine pratensis
4. Marsh Watercress, *Rorippa islandica*

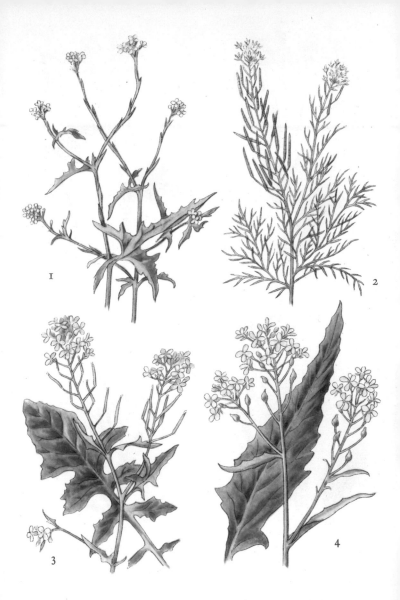

1. Hedge Mustard, *Sisymbrium officinale*
2. Flixweed, *Sisymbrium sophia*

3. Wintercress, *Barbarea vulgaris*
4. Eastern Bunias, *Bunias orientalis*

35

1. Turnip, *Brassica rapa*
2. Charlock, Wild Mustard, *Sinapis arvensis*
3. Wild Radish, *Raphanus raphanistrum*
4. Treacle Mustard, *Erysimum cheiranthoides*

1. Marsh Andromeda, *Andromeda polifolia*
2. Strawberry Tree, *Arbutus unedo*
3. Bell Heather, *Erica cinerea*
4. Blue Phyllodoce, *Phyllodoce caerulea*
5. Trailing Loiseleuria, 'Azalea', *Loiseleuria procumbens*

1. Red Bearberry, *Arctostaphylos uva-ursi*
2. Black or Alpine Bearberry, *Arctostaphylos alpina*
3. Cross-leaved Heath, *Erica tetralix*
4. Scotch Heather, Ling, *Calluna vulgaris*

1. Pontus Rhododendron,
   Rhododendron ponticum
2. Marsh Ledum, *Ledum palustre*
3. Yellow Bird's-nest, *Monotropa hypopitys*
4. Crowberry, *Empetrum nigrum*

39

1. Larger Wintergreen, *Pyrola rotundifolia*
2. Small Wintergreen, *Pyrola minor*
3. Serrated Wintergreen, *Pyrola secunda*
4. One-flowered Wintergreen, *Moneses uniflora*
5. Lapland Diapensia, *Diapensia lapponica*

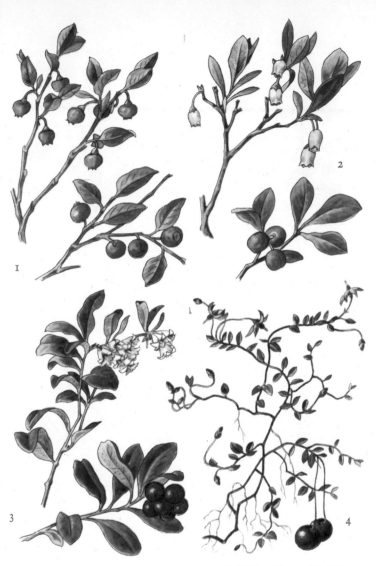

1. Bilberry, Blueberry, Whortleberry, *Vaccinium myrtillus*
2. Bog Whortleberry, *Vaccinium uliginosum*
3. Red Whortleberry, *Vaccinium vitis-idaea*
4. Cranberry, *Oxycoccus palustris*

41

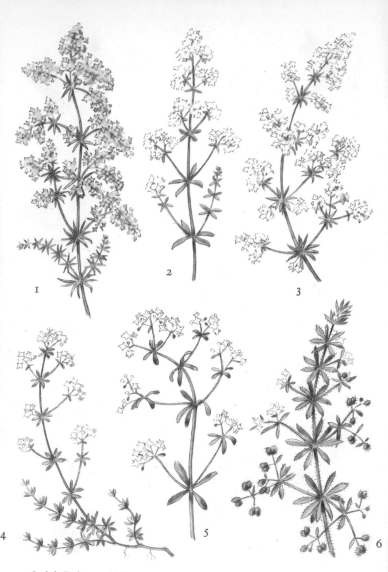

1. Lady's Bedstraw, *Galium verum*
2. Northern Bedstraw, *Galium boreale*
3. Great Hedge Bedstraw, *Galium mollugo*

4. Heath Bedstraw, *Galium saxatile*
5. Marsh Bedstraw, *Galium palustre*
6. Cleavers, Goosegrass, *Galium aparine*

42

1. Fen Bedstraw, *Galium uliginosum*
2. Woodruff, *Asperula odorata*
3. Crosswort, *Galium cruciata*
4. Field Madder, *Sherardia arvensis*
5. Periwinkle, *Vinca minor*

1. Ash, *Fraxinus excelsior*
2. Privet, *Ligustrum vulgare*

1. Elder, *Sambucus nigra*
2. Red Elder, *Sambucus racemosa*
3. Guelder Rose, *Viburnum opulus*

1. Twin-flower, *Linnaea borealis*
2. Woodbine, Honeysuckle,
   Lonicera periclymenum
3. Fly Honeysuckle, *Lonicera xylosteum*
4. Moschatel, *Adoxa moschatellina*

1. Lesser Celandine, *Ficaria verna*
2. Great Spearwort, *Ranunculus lingua*
3. Spearwort, *Ranunculus flammula*
4. Bulbous Buttercup, *Ranunculus bulbosus*

47

1. Creeping Buttercup, *Ranunculus repens*
2. Meadow Crowfoot, *Ranunculus acris*
3. Goldilocks, *Ranunculus auricomus*
4. Celery-leaved Buttercup, *Ranunculus sceleratus*

1. Hungerweed, Corn Buttercup,
   Ranunculus arvensis
2. Water Buttercup, *Ranunculus aquatilis*
3. Mousetail, *Myosurus minimus*
4. Three-lobed Hepatica, *Hepatica triloba*

1. Wood Anemone, *Anemone nemorosa*
2. Yellow Wood Anemone,
   Anemone ranunculoides
3. Pasque Flower, *Anemone pulsatilla*
4. Pheasant's Eye, *Adonis annua*
5. Ivy-leaved Crowfoot, *Ranunculus
   hederaceus*

1. Yellow Meadow-Rue, *Thalictrum flavum*
2. Traveller's Joy, Old Man's Beard, *Clematis vitalba*
3. Alpine Meadow-Rue, *Thalictrum alpinum*
4. Marsh Marigold, *Caltha palustris*

1. Globe Flower, *Trollius europaeus*
2. Larkspur, *Delphinium ajacis*

3. Columbine, *Aquilegia vulgaris*
4. Herb Christopher, Baneberry,
   Actaea spicata

1. White Water-Lily, *Nymphaea alba*
2. Brandy Bottle, Yellow Water-Lily, *Nuphar lutea*
3. Greater Celandine, *Chelidonium majus*
4. Fumitory, *Fumaria officinalis*

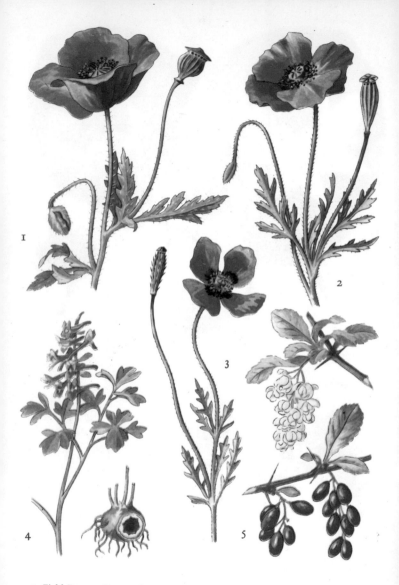

1. Field Poppy, *Papaver rhoeas*
2. Long-headed Poppy, *Papaver dubium*
3. Pale Poppy, *Papaver argemone*

4. Hollow Corydalis, *Corydalis cava*
5. Barberry, *Berberis vulgaris*

1. Bladder Campion, *Silene cucubalus*
2. Nodding Silene (Nottingham Catchfly), *Silene nutans*
3. Spanish Catchfly, *Silene otites*
4. Moss Campion, *Silene acaulis*
5. Ragged Robin, *Lychnis flos-cuculi*

55

1. White Campion, *Lychnis alba*   3. Viscid Lychnis, *Lychnis viscaria*
2. Red Campion, *Lychnis dioica*   4. Alpine Lychnis, *Lychnis alpina*

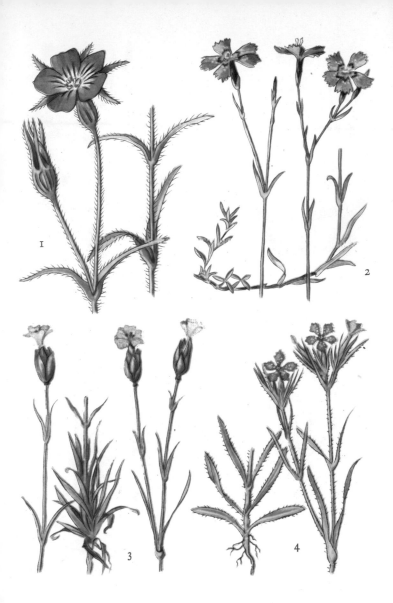

1. Corn Cockle, *Lychnis githago*
2. Maiden Pink, *Dianthus deltoides*
3. Proliferous Pink, *Dianthus prolifer*
4. Deptford Pink, *Dianthus armeria*

1. Wood Starwort, *Stellaria nemorum*
2. Chickweed, *Stellaria media*
3. Greater Stitchwort, Great Starwort,
   Stellaria holostea
4. Heath Stitchwort, *Stellaria graminea*
5. Field Chickweed, *Cerastium arvense*

1. Alpine Mouse-ear Chickweed,
   Cerastium alpinum
2. Common Mouse-ear Chickweed,
   Cerastium vulgatum
3. Little Mouse-ear Chickweed,
   Cerastium semidecandrum
4. Thyme-leaved Sandwort,
   Arenaria serpyllifolia
5. Three-nerved Sandwort,
   Arenaria trinervia
6. Sea Purslane, *Arenaria peploides*

1. Knotted Pearlwort, *Sagina nodosa*
2. Procumbent Pearlwort, *Sagina procumbens*
3. Spurry, *Spergula arvensis*
4. Sand Spurry, *Spergularia rubra*
5. Rupture Wort, *Herniaria glabra*
6. Annual Knawel, *Scleranthus annuus*

60

1. Goosefoot, Fat Hen, *Chenopodium album*
2. Hastate Orache, *Atriplex hastata*
3. Common Orache, *Atriplex patula*
4. Shore Orache, *Atriplex littoralis*
5. Marsh Glasswort or Samphire, *Salicornia herbacea*

61

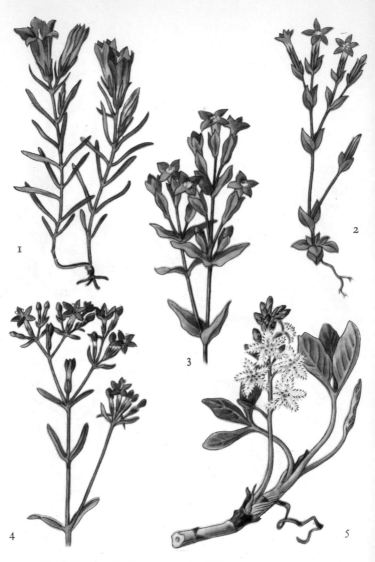

1. Marsh Gentian, *Gentiana pneumonanthe*
2. Small Alpine Gentian, *Gentiana nivalis*
3. Field Gentian, *Gentiana campestris*
4. Centaury, *Centaurium minus*
5. Buckbean, *Menyanthes trifoliata*

1. Butterwort, *Pinguicula vulgaris*
2. Bladderwort, *Utricularia vulgaris*
3. Cowslip, *Primula veris*
4. Mealy or Bird's Eye Primrose, *Primula farinosa*
5. Northern Androsace, *Androsace septentrionalis*

1. Water Violet, *Hottonia palustris*
2. Trientale, *Trientalis europaea*
3. Sea Milkwort, *Glaux maritima*
4. Scarlet Pimpernel, Poor Man's
   Weather-glass, *Anagallis arvensis*

1. Greater Plantain, *Plantago major*
2. Hoary Plantain, *Plantago media*
3. Ribwort Plantain, *Plantago lanceolata*
4. Sea Plantain, *Plantago maritima*
5. Buckshorn Plantain, *Plantago coronopus*

65

1. Yellow Loosestrife, *Lysimachia*
   vulgaris
2. Creeping Jenny, Moneywort,
   Lysimachia nummularia

3. Tufted Loosestrife, *Lysimachia*
   thyrsiflora
4. Sea Thrift, *Armeria maritima*

66

1. Viviparous Polygonum,
   Polygonum viviparum
2. Floating Polygonum,
   Polygonum amphibium
3. Peachwort, Red-shanks,
   Polygonum persicaria
4. Waterpepper,
   Polygonum hydropiper
5. Black Bindweed,
   Polygonum convolvulus
6. Knotweed, Knotgrass,
   Polygonum aviculare

1. Sheep Sorrel, *Rumex acetosella*
2. Sorrel, *Rumex acetosa*
3. Grainless Curled Dock, *Rumex longifolius*
4. Curled Dock, *Rumex crispus*
5. Kidney Sorrel, *Oxyria digyna*

1. Rose Bay, *Chamaenerion angustifolium*
2. Great Willow Herb, Codlins-and-Cream, *Epilobium hirsutum*
3. Mountain Willow Herb, *Epilobium montanum*
4. Marsh Willow Herb, *Epilobium palustre*
5. Alpine Willow Herb, *Epilobium alpinum*
6. Enchanter's Nightshade, *Circaea lutetiana*

1. Marestail, *Hippuris vulgaris*
2. Sea Buckthorn, *Hippophae rhamnoides*
3. Mezereon, Spurge Olive, *Daphne mezereum*
4. Purple Loosestrife, *Lythrum salicaria*

1. Rose-root Stonecrop, *Sedum roseum*
2. Orpine, Livelong, *Sedum telephium*
3. Spurious Stonecrop, *Sedum spurium*
4. Stonecrop, *Sedum acre*
5. White Sedum, *Sedum album*

71

1. Star Saxifrage, *Saxifraga stellaris*
2. Alpine Saxifrage, *Saxifraga nivalis*
3. Purple Saxifrage, *Saxifraga oppositifolia*
4. Yellow Mountain Saxifrage, *Saxifraga aizoides*
5. Drooping Saxifrage, *Saxifraga cernua*

1. Marsh Saxifrage, *Saxifraga hirculus*
2. Rue-leaved Saxifrage, *Saxifraga tridactylites*
3. Meadow Saxifrage, *Saxifraga granulata*
4. Alternate Golden Saxifrage, *Chrysosplenium alternifolium*
5. Grass of Parnassus, *Parnassia palustris*

73

1. Pimpinel, Burnet Saxifrage,
   Pimpinella saxifraga
2. Caraway, *Carum carvi*
3. Goutweed, Bishop's Weed, Herb Gerrard,
   Aegopodium podagraria
4. Wood Sanicle, *Sanicula europaea*
5. Sea Holly, *Eryngium maritimum*

1. Wild Parsnip, *Pastinaca sativa*
2. Fool's Parsley, *Aethusa cynapium*
3. Cowbane, Water Hemlock, *Cicuta virosa*
4. Water Parsnip, *Sium latifolium*

1. Wild Angelica,
   Angelica sylvestris
2. Garden Archangelica,
   Archangelica officinalis
3. Marsh Hog's Fennel, Milk Parsley,
   Peucedanum palustre
4. Cow Parsnip, Hogweed,
   Heracleum spondylium

1. Sweet Cicely, *Myrrhis odorata*
2. Wild Parsley, Keck, *Anthriscus sylvestris*
3. Hemlock, *Conium maculatum*
4. Wild Carrot, *Daucus carota*

1. Field Scabious, *Knautia arvensis*
2. Devil's Bit, *Succisa pratensis*
3. Cornsalad, Lamb's Lettuce, *Valerianella olitoria*
4. Valerian, *Valeriana officinalis*

1. Broad-leaved Campanula, Throatwort,
   Campanula latifolia
2. Nettle-leaved Campanula,
   Campanula trachelium
3. Creeping Bell-flower,
   Campanula rapunculoides
4. Peach-leaved Bell-flower,
   Campanula persicifolia

1. Water Lobelia, *Lobelia dortmanna*
2. Sheep's Bit, *Jasione montana*
3. Clustered Bell-flower, *Campanula glomerata*
4. Spreading Campanula, *Campanula patula*
5. Harebell, Bluebell, *Campanula rotundifolia*

1. Yellow Chamomile, *Anthemis tinctoria*
2. Corn Chamomile, *Anthemis arvensis*
3. Scentless Matricary, *Matricaria inodora*
4. Wild Chamomile, *Matricaria chamomilla*

1. Three-lobed Bur-Marigold, *Bidens tripartita*
2. Nodding Bur-Marigold, *Bidens cernua*
3. Yarrow, Milfoil, *Achillea millefolium*
4. Sneezewort Yarrow, *Achillea ptarmica*

1. Mugwort, *Artemisia vulgaris*
2. Field Mugwort, *Artemisia campestris*
3. Wormwood, *Artemisia absinthium*
4. Goldilocks-Aster, Goldilocks,
   Aster linosyris

1. Rayless Chamomile, *Matricaria matricarioides*
2. Ox-Eye, Dog-Daisy, *Chrysanthemum leucanthemum*
3. Corn-Marigold, *Chrysanthemum segetum*
4. Tansy, *Tanacetum vulgare*

1. Groundsel, *Senecio vulgaris*   3. Ragwort, *Senecio jacobaea*
2. Sticky Groundsel, *Senecio viscosus*   4. Hemp Agrimony, *Eupatorium cannabinum*

1. Coltsfoot, *Tussilago farfara*
2. Butterbur, *Petasites hybridus*
3. Cat's-ear, Mountain Everlasting,
   Antennaria dioica
4. Willow-leaved Fleabane, *Inula salicina*

1. Wood or Heath Cudweed,
   Gnaphalium sylvaticum
2. Dwarf Cudweed, *Gnaphalium
   supinum*
3. Marsh Cudweed, *Gnaphalium
   uliginosum*
4. Marsh Senecio, *Senecio
   palustris*

1. Slender Cudweed, *Filago minima*   3. Sea Aster, *Aster tripolium*
2. Goldenrod, *Solidago virgaurea*   4. Daisy, *Bellis perennis*

1. Alpine Saussurea, *Saussurea alpina*
2. Greater Knapweed, *Centaurea scabiosa*
3. Brown-rayed Knapweed, *Centaurea jacea*
4. Bluebottle, Cornflower, *Centaurea cyanus*

1. Melancholy Thistle, *Cirsium helenioides*
2. Stemless Thistle, *Cirsium acaule*

3. Creeping Thistle, *Cirsium arvense*
4. Sawwort, *Serratula tinctoria*

90

1. Woolly Burdock, *Arctium tomentosum*
2. Lesser Burdock, *Arctium minus*
3. Carline Thistle, *Carlina vulgaris*
4. Spiny Thistle, *Carduus acanthoides*

1. Welted Thistle, *Carduus crispus*
2. Spear Thistle, *Cirsium lanceolatum*
3. Marsh Thistle, *Cirsium palustre*
4. Water Thistle, *Cirsium oleraceum*

1. Fleabane, *Erigeron acris*
2. One-headed Fleabane, *Erigeron uniflorum*
3. Goat's Beard Salsify, *Tragopogon pratensis*
4. Low Scorzonera, *Scorzonera humilis*

1. Dandelion, *Taraxacum vulgare*
2. Autumn Hawkbit, *Leontodon autumnalis*
3. Spotted Cat's-ear, *Hypochaeris maculata*
4. Mouse-ear Hawkweed, *Hieracium pilosella*

1. Umbellate Hawkweed,
   Hieracium umbellatum
2. Orange-flowered Hawkweed,
   Hieracium aurantiacum
3. Corn Sowthistle, *Sonchus arvensis*
4. Common Sowthistle, *Sonchus oleraceus*

1. Blue Sowthistle, *Mulgedium alpinum*   3. Nipplewort, *Lapsana communis*
2. Wall Lettuce, *Lactuca muralis*   4. Chicory, *Cichorium intybus*

96

1. Bloody Crane's Bill, *Geranium sanguineum*
2. Wood Crane's Bill, *Geranium sylvaticum*
3. Small-flowered Crane's Bill, *Geranium pusillum*
4. Shining Crane's Bill, *Geranium lucidum*
5. Herb Robert, *Geranium robertianum*

97

1. Stork's Bill, *Erodium cicutarium*
2. Touch-me-not, *Impatiens noli–tangere*
3. Purging Flax, *Linum catharticum*
4. Wood-Sorrel, *Oxalis acetosella*
5. Milkwort, *Polygala vulgaris*

1. Water Forget-me-not, *Myosotis palustris*
2. Wood Forget-me-not, *Myosotis sylvatica*
3. Field Myosotis, *Myosotis arvensis*
4. Lungwort, *Pulmonaria officinalis*
5. Hound's Tongue, *Cynoglossum officinale*

1. Common Alkanet, *Anchusa officinalis*
2. Bugloss, *Lycopsis arvensis*
3. Corn Gromwell, *Lithospermum arvense*
4. Comfrey, *Symphytum officinale*
5. Viper's Bugloss, *Echium vulgare*

1. Bindweed, *Convolvulus arvensis*
2. Large-flowered Bindweed,
   Calystegia sepium
3. Greater Dodder, *Cuscuta europaea*
4. Jacob's Ladder, *Polemonium
   caeruleum*

1. Tea Plant, *Lycium chinense*
2. Bittersweet, *Solanum dulcamara*
3. Black Nightshade, *Solanum nigrum*
4. Henbane, *Hyoscyamus niger*

1. Great Mullein or Aaron's Rod, *Verbascum thapsus*
2. Black Mullein, *Verbascum nigrum*
3. Figwort, *Scrophularia nodosa*
4. Foxglove, *Digitalis purpurea*

1. Purple Cow-wheat,
   Melampyrum arvense
2. Greater Broomrape, *Orobanche major*
3. Marsh Lousewort, *Pedicularis palustris*
4. Lousewort, *Pedicularis sylvatica*
5. Water Veronica, *Veronica anagallis-aquatica*

1. Common Cow-wheat, *Melampyrum pratense*
2. Wood Cow-wheat, *Melampyrum sylvaticum*
3. Crested Melampyrum, *Melampyrum cristatum*
4. Toothwort, *Lathraea squamaria*

1. Alpine Speedwell, *Veronica alpina*
2. Spicate Speedwell, *Veronica spicata*
3. Eyebright, *Euphrasia officinalis*
4. Red Bartsia, *Bartsia odontites*
5. Alpine Bartsia, *Bartsia alpina*
6. Common Corn Rattle, *Rhinanthus minor*

1. Germander Speedwell, *Veronica chamaedrys*
2. Field Speedwell, *Veronica agrestis*
3. Ivy-leaved Speedwell, *Veronica hederifolia*
4. Vernal Speedwell, *Veronica verna*
5. Wall Speedwell, *Veronica arvensis*
6. Thyme-leaved Speedwell *Veronica serpyllifolia*

107

1. Yellow Toad Flax, *Linaria vulgaris*
2. Marsh Speedwell, *Veronica scutellata*
3. Brook-lime Speedwell, *Veronica beccabunga*
4. Common Speedwell, *Veronica officinalis*

1. Skullcap, *Scutellaria galericulata*
2. Motherwort, *Leonurus cardiaca*
3. Hedge Stachys, *Stachys sylvatica*
4. Marsh Stachys, *Stachys palustris*

1. Wild Basil, *Clinopodium vulgare*
2. Field Calamint, *Clinopodium acinos*
3. Ground Ivy, *Nepeta hederacea*
4. Common Bugle, *Ajuga reptans*
5. Self-heal, *Prunella vulgaris*

110

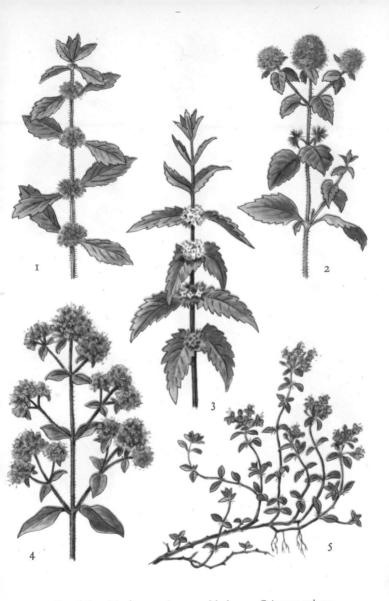

1. Corn Mint, *Mentha arvensis*
2. Water Mint, *Mentha aquatica*
3. Gipsywort, *Lycopus europaeus*
4. Marjoram, *Origanum vulgare*
5. Wild Thyme, *Thymus serpyllum*

1. Henbit, *Lamium amplexicaule*
2. Red Dead Nettle, *Lamium purpureum*
3. Deadnettle, *Lamium album*
4. Yellow Archangel, *Lamium galeobdolon*
5. Hemp Nettle, *Galeopsis tetrahit*
6. Large-flowered Hemp Nettle, *Galeopsis speciosa*

1. Water Plantain, *Alisma plantago-aquatica*
2. Arrowhead, *Sagittaria sagittifolia*
3. Canadian Elodea, *Elodea canadensis*
4. Broad-leaved Pondweed,
   Potamogeton natans
5. Perfoliate Pondweed,
   Potamogeton perfoliatum

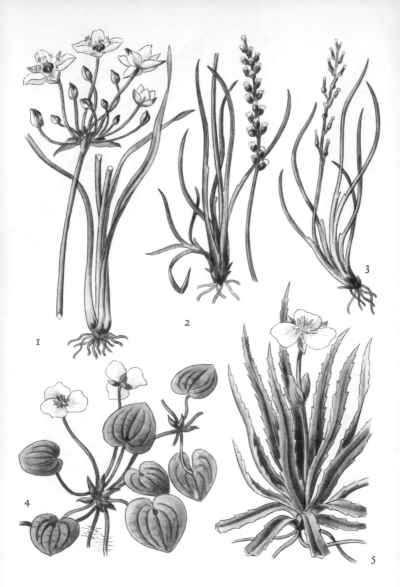

1. Flowering Rush, *Butomus umbellatus*
2. Sea Arrowgrass, *Triglochin maritima*
3. Marsh Arrowgrass, *Triglochin palustris*
4. Frogbit, *Hydrocharis morsus-ranae*
5. Water Soldier, *Stratiotes aloides*

114

1. Bur-reed, *Sparganium ramosum*
2. Great Reedmace, Cat's-tail, *Typha latifolia*
3. Marsh Calla, *Calla palustris*
4. Lesser Duckweed, *Lemna minor*
5. Ivy-leaved Duckweed, *Lemna trisulca*

1. Angular Solomon's-seal,
   Polygonatum officinale
2. Lily of the Valley,
   Convallaria majalis
3. May Lily, *Maianthemum bifolium*
4. Herb Paris, *Paris quadrifolia*

1. Bog Asphodel, *Narthecium ossifragum*   3. Yellow Flag, *Iris pseudacorus*
2. Scottish Asphodel, *Tofieldia pusilla*   4. Snake's Head, *Fritillaria meleagris*

1. Yellow Star of Bethlehem,
   Gagea lutea
2. Wild Tulip, *Tulipa sylvestris*
3. Ramsons, *Allium ursinum*
4. Field Garlic, *Allium oleraceum*
5. Chives, *Allium schoenoprasum*

1. Military Orchis, *Orchis militaris*
2. Dwarf Orchis, *Orchis ustulata*
3. Green-winged Orchis, *Orchis morio*
4. Early Orchis, *Orchis mascula*
5. Pyramidal Orchid, *Anacamptis pyramidalis*

119

1. Straight-leaved Orchis, *Orchis strictifolia*
2. Spotted Orchis, *Orchis maculata*
3. Fragrant Orchid, *Gymnadenia conopsea*
4. Lesser Butterfly Orchid, *Platanthera bifolia*

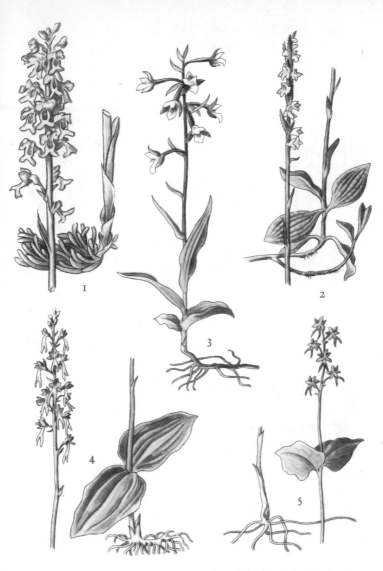

1. Bird's Nest Orchid, *Neottia nidus-avis*
2. Creeping Ladies Tresses, *Goodyera repens*
3. Marsh Helleborine, *Epipactis palustris*
4. Twayblade, *Listera ovata*
5. Lesser Twayblade, *Listera cordata*

1. Common Rush, *Juncus effusus*
2. Field Woodrush, *Luzula campestris*
3. Hairy Woodrush, *Luzula pilosa*
4. Sea Scirpus, *Scirpus maritimus*
5. Bulrush, *Scirpus lacustris*
6. Common Cotton Grass, *Eriophorum angustifolium*
7. Rusty Bog-Rush, *Schoenus ferrugineus*

1. Sand Carex, *Carex arenaria*
2. Fingered Sedge, *Carex digitata*
3. Spring Sedge, *Carex caryophyllea*
4. Beaked Carex, *Carex rostrata*
5. Black Sedge, *Carex atrata*
6. Carnation Grass, *Carex panicea*
7. Common Sedge, *Carex nigra*
8. Tufted Sedge, *Carex acuta*

123

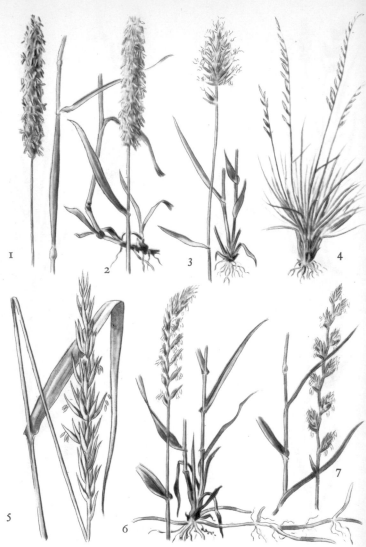

1. Meadow Foxtail, *Alopecurus pratensis*
2. Timothy Grass, Cat's-tail, *Phleum pratense*
3. Sweet Vernal Grass, *Anthoxanthum odoratum*
4. Mat-grass, *Nardus stricta*
5. Lyme Grass, *Elymus arenarius*
6. Couch or Twitch Grass, *Agropyron repens*
7. Perennial Rye Grass, *Lolium perenne*

124

1. Field Brome, *Bromus arvensis*
2. Soft Brome, Lop Grass, *Bromus mollis*
3. Sheep's Fescue, *Festuca ovina*
4. Red or Creeping Fescue, *Festuca rubra*
5. Meadow Fescue, *Festuca pratensis*
6. Crested Dog's tail, *Cynosurus cristatus*

125

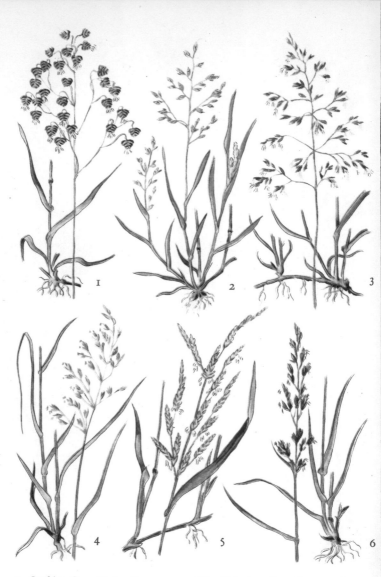

1. Quaking Grass, Totter Grass,
   Briza media
2. Annual Meadow Grass, *Poa annua*
3. Meadow Grass, *Poa pratensis*
4. Wood Meadow Grass, *Poa nemoralis*
5. Floating Sweet Grass, *Glyceria fluitans*
6. Purple Moor Grass, *Molinia caerulea*

126

1. Common Reed,
   Phragmites communis
2. Mountain or Nodding
   Melick, *Melica nutans*
3. Blue Moor Grass, *Sesleria
   caerulea, var. calcarea*
4. Tall or False Oat Grass,
   Arrhenatherum elatius
5. Wavy Hair Grass,
   Deschampsia flexuosa
6. Tufted Hair Grass,
   Deschampsia caespitosa

1. Yorkshire Fog, *Holcus lanatus*
2. Marram Grass, *Ammophila arenaria*
3. Purple Small Reed, *Calamagrostis canescens*
4. Wood Small Reed or Bush Grass, *Calamagrostis epigejos*
5. Common Bent or Brown Top, *Agrostis tenuis*
6. Cocksfoot, *Dactylis glomerata*

DESCRIPTIONS

1 SCOTS PINE, *Pinus sylvestris*. A lovely evergreen tree up to about 1
80 ft high, with flaky bark; branches of 2 kinds, long and short
shoots, the latter bearing a pair of needle-like leaves; male 'cones'
crowded towards the top of the shoot, emitting clouds of pollen
at the end of May; female cones solitary, opening on warm
summer days and releasing the seeds winged at one end.

2 NORWAY SPRUCE, *Picea abies*. Large tree with drooping branchlets; bark reddish brown; buds ovoid, acute, not resinous, the
scales often with spreading tips; branches in whorls; leaves up to
1 in. long, acute, dark green and shining; cones pendulous,
cylindric, 4–5 in. long, light brown, purple or green before matur-
ity; scales thin, with toothed apex; introduced into plantations;
valuable timber.

3 JUNIPER, *Juniperus communis*. Evergreen spiny shrub with narrow
very sharply pointed leaves in whorls of 3; flowers in spring, very
small, yellow, in small cones; 'fruits' dark-purple-blue, about
⅓ in. across, used for flavouring gin; on open downs in chalky
districts.

4 YEW, *Taxus baccata*. A small tree of sombre aspect often planted
near a church or used as a hedge, but truly wild on chalky downs;
leaves very narrow, spreading in one plane; male flowers in little
yellow clusters on one tree, the solitary female flowers on a separate tree; 'fruits' very poisonous, enclosed in a red fleshy cup-like
structure (aril) eaten by birds.

1 INTERMEDIATE WHITE BEAM, *Sorbus intermedia*. Large tree, 2
with long and short shoots, the latter bearing a bunch of obovate-
elliptic leaves lobulate and serrate, glabrous above, whitish-woolly
beneath; flowers white in corymbs terminating the short annual
shoots; stalks and calyx very woolly; ovary densely woolly
styles 2; fruits becoming hairless except the remains of the calyx,
the size of a black grape but bright red.

2 ROWAN, MOUNTAIN ASH, *Sorbus aucuparia*. Elegant tree up to
30 ft; bark greyish, smooth; leaves alternate, pinnate, with about
6–8 pairs of leaflets and an end-leaflet; flowers creamy-white,
densely arranged in a flat corymb, scented; stamens 20–25; styles
usually 3; fruit globose, scarlet or rarely orange, soon eaten by
birds; wood hard, with a fine grain; May.

3 1 CRAB APPLE, *Malus pumila.* One of our most beautiful native trees up to 45 ft, both in flower and fruit as well as for autumn colour; leaves scattered on the long shoots, clustered on the short shoots; flowers strongly scented at night and attract numerous night-flying insects; fruits sour but make excellent jelly; occurs wild from the Forth and Clyde southwards; May.

2 HAWTHORN, MAY, *Crataegus oxyacanthoides.* Shrub or small tree used extensively as a hedge; branchlets ending in sharp thorns; leaves on very short annual shoots, coarsely toothed or pinnately lobed; flowers white or pinkish-white, fragrant, in short corymbs; anthers reddish; ovary inferior, with 2–3 free styles; fruit a small almost globose red berry crowned by the calyx; May–June; fruit valuable bird food.

3 SLOE, *Prunus spinosa.* Small tree; small white flowers produced in early spring before the leaves, on short lateral spine-tipped branchlets; fruits blue-black and globular or broadly elliptic, extremely sour, but making fairly good jam; formerly used in making British Port Wine and the juice for marking-ink; wood tough and used as teeth for rakes.

4 1 WILD CHERRY, GEAN, *Prunus avium.* Tree up to 100 ft high; bark thin, smooth, grey, peeling off in transverse stripes; branches composed of long shoots and short shoots; leaves with a pair of glands at the base; flowers produced with the leaves, clustered on the short shoots, white; fruit globose, reddish; wood a valuable timber with a fine even grain; spring.

2 BIRD CHERRY, HECKBERRY, *Padus racemosa.* Small tree or shrub; flowers white, strongly scented, in May; leaves serrate, with 2 glands at the base; stipules in pairs, soon falling off; petals slightly toothed; fruit small, globose, black and shining with a hard stone in the middle, extremely bitter, making the tongue nearly black; eaten by birds; in woods and hedges mainly in northern Britain.

5 1 MEADOWSWEET, *Filipendula ulmaria.* Perennial up to 4 ft; in wet meadows and near water; basal leaves large, pinnate; terminal leaflets deeply 3–4-lobed, lateral leaflets toothed, alternating with pairs of quite small leaflets, all often with a dense felt of hairs below; stipules leaf-like; flowers crowded in a cyme, creamy-white; stamens numerous; carpels free, becoming twisted in fruit.

2 DROPWORT, *Filipendula vulgaris*. Perennial herb with roots swollen here and there into oblong tubers; stem up to 2 ft; leaves mostly crowded at base of stem, pinnately divided into alternately larger and smaller leaflets; flowers white or tinged with red, in a terminal cyme; carpels free, not twisted in fruit; mainly in chalky and limestone pastures; summer.

3 AGRIMONY, *Agrimonia eupatoria*. Perennial herb in dry thickets, hedgebanks and sides of fields, up to 3 ft; no basal leaves; stem-leaves pinnate, with coarsely toothed leaflets with smaller leaflets between them; stipules large, leafy; all covered with soft hairs; flowers yellow, spicate; fruits with a ring of hooked bristles at the top; summer, autumn.

4 COMMON AVENS, HERB BENNETT, *Geum urbanum*. Perennial herb on hedgebanks and margins of woods, roots formerly used to impart a clove-like flavour to ale; basal leaves pinnate with a large lobed end-leaflet; stipules large and leafy; flowers terminal, bright yellow; stamens numerous; carpels numerous, free, in fruit prolonged into hooked prickles; spring to autumn.

1 WATER AVENS, *Geum rivale*. Perennial herb in marshy places **6** and ditches; basal leaves on long hairy stalks, irregularly pinnate, end-leaflet largest, coarsely toothed and lobed, thinly hairy; stem-leaves much smaller; flowers nodding; calyx reddish brown; petals yellow, streaked with red, strongly nerved; carpels in a stalked bunch, style persistent and hooked in fruit; summer.

2 LADY'S MANTLE, *Alchemilla vulgaris*. Perennial herb; basal leaves on long stalks, kidney-shaped in outline, shortly and broadly 5-7-lobed fan-wise, green on both sides; flowers very small, greenish yellow, in small irregular clusters with leafy bracts; no petals; stamens 4; style 1 from the base of the one carpel; spring, summer.

3 ALPINE LADY'S MANTLE, *Alchemilla alpina*. Very similar to Lady's Mantle, but easily recognized by the shining silvery hairs which clothe stems and under surface of the leaves, the latter more deeply divided into narrow nearly entire parts; flowers yellow in small dense corymbs; no petals; stamens 4; northern Britain and Eire; summer.

4 SIBBALD'S POTENTILLA, *Potentilla sibbaldii*. Perennial with creeping rootstock, forming dense spreading tufts; leaves long-stalked, divided into 3 leaflets, these obovate-wedge-shaped,

deeply 3-toothed only at the top, bristly hairy on both sides; flowers small, in stalked clusters; petals 5 or absent, narrow and very small; stamens 5–7; achenes mostly 5; style lateral; northern England and Scotland; summer.

5 MOUNTAIN AVENS, *Dryas octopetala*. Woody perennial; stems much branched, prostrate or creeping, forming dense tufts; stipules thin, united with the leaf-stalks; leaves oblong, deeply toothed, green above, snow-white beneath; flowers white on long slender hairy stalks; sepals about 8, narrow; petals 8–10, free, white; stamens numerous; achenes with long silky tails; mostly limestone soil in northern Britain; June–July.

7 1 SHRUBBY CINQUEFOIL, *Potentilla fruticosa*. Erect much-branched shrub up to 2½ ft; bark splitting lengthwise; annual shoots and leaves covered with long silvery silky hairs; leaves pinnately divided into 5 narrow entire leaflets; flowers numerous but single, yellow; carpels numerous, with a basal style; limestone districts in northern England and in Eire; summer.

2 SILVERY-LEAVED CINQUEFOIL, *Potentilla argentea*. Low perennial; leaves white below with short woolly hairs, blade divided to the base into 5 pairs, each part narrowly wedge-shaped and deeply lobed; flowers in short leafy cymes; petals 5, bright yellow, rounded; stamens several; carpels numerous, surrounded by shaggy white hairs; styles terminal; in dry sunny pastures, heaths; summer.

3 SPRING CINQUEFOIL, *Potentilla verna*. In habit very like the Alpine Lady's Mantle but with broader leaflets toothed around the upper part; lower leaves long-stalked, sometimes with 7 leaflets, upper becoming sessile; flowers at the ends of short weak branches, like small buttercups, the petals yellow, broad and longer than the calyx; stamens numerous; carpels numerous; spring and summer.

4 ERECT POTENTILLA, *Potentilla erecta*. Perennial herb with numerous slender erect hairy stems from a thick rootstock; leaves nearly stalkless, divided to the base into 3 narrow parts with a pair of leafy lobed stipules at the base; flowers on slender stalks, yellow; stamens 15–20; carpels few, hairy around the base, reticulate in fruit; heaths and dry pastures; summer.

8 1 CREEPING CINQUEFOIL, *Potentilla reptans*. Perennial herb with creeping stems rooting at the nodes; leaves on long slender stalks divided fan-wise into 5 separate coarsely toothed leaflets; flowers $\frac{3}{4}$–1 in. diam., single on slender long stalks; petals 5, bright yellow; carpels numerous, inserted on a hairy conical axis; meadows and roadsides; summer and autumn.

2 SILVER WEED, *Potentilla anserina*. Perennial giving off procumbent runners; leaves all from the root, pinnate, silky and silvery-white on both sides; leaflets up to 15 pairs with smaller leaflets between; flowers single on long stalks; petals 5, yellow; carpels numerous, the slender style near the top; damp meadows and banks of ditches and by roadsides; flowers close up at night; summer.

3 MARSH CINQUEFOIL, *Potentilla palustris*. Perennial in marshy places and spongy peat-bogs in hilly districts; lower leaves with a terminal and 2–3 pairs of lateral leaflets; stipules large, joined to leaf stalk; flowers very few in a terminal leafy cluster; calyx dark-purple, lobes pointed; petals very small; anthers purple, almost orbicular; roots yield a yellowish dye; summer.

4 WILD STRAWBERRY, *Fragaria vesca*. Just a garden strawberry in miniature and very tasty; in woods and shady banks, often on railway cuttings and embankments; leaflets 3, coarsely toothed; flowers few on a long common stalk; petals 5, white; anthers horse-shoe shaped; carpels numerous and tiny on a conical axis which enlarges and becomes the 'fruit'; spring, summer.

1 STONE BLACKBERRY, *Rubus saxatilis*. Rootstock giving off a 9 few creeping runners rooting at the nodes and short erect simple stems up to 1 ft high, hairy, sometimes with a few prickles; leaflets usually 3, pale green, obovate, serrate; flowers on slender stalks, 2–3 in the axils of the upper leaves; petals whitish or greenish yellow, narrow; berries red, with few carpels; in open woods; summer.

2 CLOUDBERRY, *Rubus chamaemorus*. Dwarf perennial herb of northern moors and mountains; leaves 1–3 on each plant, rounded, deeply 5-lobed, 5 nerved from the base; flowers of one sex, solitary, terminal; petals 5, white, $\frac{3}{4}$ in. long; stamens numerous; carpels several, orange-yellow when ripe; summer.

3 ARCTIC BLACKBERRY, *Rubus arcticus*. Stem dwarf, up to 8 in. arising from a creeping rootstock; leaves 3-foliolate, leaflets rounded-ovate to obovate, coarsely and bluntly toothed, up to $1\frac{1}{4}$ in. long, hairless or nearly so; flowers usually solitary, $\frac{3}{4}$ in.

diam.; petals 5–7, rounded, notched, deep rose; fruit a few red amber drupes, sweet and palatable; June; introduced in and around rock gardens; Swedish people make a syrup, jelly and wine from the berries.

4 DEWBERRY, *Rubus caesius*. Very like the common Blackberry, but branches spreading or creeping along the ground; flowers few, in small terminal panicles; sepals narrow, pointed, clasping the fruit, the latter covered by a glaucous bloom like that of grapes; in open fields and stony places; summer.

10 1 RASPBERRY, *Rubus idaeus*. Stems biennial, flowering and fruiting the second season, prickly; leaves pinnate, lower often with 2, upper with 1 pair of leaflets and an end-leaflet, with a soft felt of hairs below; stipules narrow, paired; flowers few together, white; carpels numerous on a conical axis, becoming red or yellow and juicy in fruit; in woods and on railway embankments; June.

2 BLACKBERRY, *Rubus fruticosus*. Perennial with biennial flowering stems or sometimes lasting longer, mostly arched and often rooting when touching the soil, very prickly; stipules narrow; leaflets large and coarse, 3 or 5, ovate, dentate, often hairy, the midribs and stalks prickly; flowers white or pink in terminal panicles; fruit black or dull red, the calyx usually reflexed; summer, fruiting in September–October.

3 DOG ROSE, *Rosa canina*. Shrub; branches prickly; leaves with usually 2 pairs of leaflets and a terminal one, and a large 2-lobed stipule joined to the stalk; flowers sweet-scented, $1\frac{1}{2}$–2 in. diam., usually only one open at a time in each cluster of 3; sepals toothed; petals white or pink; fruits red, usually 3 together, sepals falling off; fruits rich in vitamin C, providing Rose-hip Syrup; June.

11 1 SMALL-LEAVED LIME, *Tilia cordata*. Tree up to 100 ft; leaves long-stalked, rounded-cordate, about $2\frac{1}{2}$ in. long and broad, serrate, dark green above, bluish or glaucous-green below, hairy in the axils of the nerves below; flowers in a small erect umbel with a long veiny bract adnate to the common stalk in lower half; ranges in wild state from Cumberland southwards; June.

2 MOUNTAIN RIBES, *Ribes alpinum*. A much branched shrub or shrublet; leaves alternate, deeply and irregularly divided and toothed, smooth and shining; flowers yellow, of one sex, the males rather numerous in little erect racemes, the females on

separate plants, fewer together, in very short racemes and almost sessile; berries red, small and tasteless; northern Britain; spring.

3 ENTIRE-LEAVED COTONEASTER, *Cotoneaster integerrimus*. Only found wild in North Wales; a dwarf deep-rooted shrub with long and short shoots; leaves broadly ovate-elliptic to nearly rounded, 1–2 in. long, densely woolly below; flowers few at ends of short shoots; petals 5, erect, pink, finely veined; stamens numerous; ovary inferior, of 3 carpels with lateral styles; fruit a red berry; spring.

1 SEA PEA, *Lathyrus japonicus*. Perennial with long thick black **12** rootstock; stems sharply angled; leaves pale glaucous-green, pinnate, ending in a 2–3-forked tendril; stipules large and like the leaflets; flowers few in erect stalked racemes, purple, fading to blue; fruits compressed like a pea, nearly 2 in. long; seeds nearly black; only on shingle beaches in south-eastern England from Suffolk to Dorset and in Shetlands.

2 MEADOW PEA, *Lathyrus pratensis*. Perennial herb; stems sharply angled; leaves with only 1 pair of leaflets with 3 parallel nerves and a simple or branched tendril; flowers bright yellow, several on an axillary common stalk; fruits 1¾ in. long, compressed; seeds dark brown or olive mottled with black.

3 TUBEROUS PEA, *Lathyrus montanus*. Perennial herb with creeping rootstock swollen like tubers at some of the nodes; stems erect, angled; leaves with 2–3 pairs of narrow leaflets with 3–5 parallel nerves, axis ending in a long sharp point; flowers few in terminal and axillary racemes, bright reddish-purple fading to brown; fruits about 2 in. long, finely reticulate; seeds brown; in woodlands and on heaths.

4 TUFTED VETCH, *Vicia cracca*. Perennial with slender annual stems 4–5 ft long or more, climbing over hedges and bushes; leaves with numerous narrow leaflets and the common stalk ending in a branched tendril; flowers very numerous in one-sided racemes and more or less reflexed, bluish-purple; fruits flat, about 1½ in. long, with several dark velvety brown seeds; July, August.

5 BUSH or HEDGE VETCH, *Vicia sepium*. Perennial herb; leaves spreading or recurved, pinnate, leaflets nearly opposite, common stalk ending in several slender threads; flowers few in the leaf-axils, dull lilac to pale purple, yellowish at base; fruits 1–1½ in. long, like small pea-pods, curling up after opening; seeds purple-black.

13 1 MILK VETCH, *Astragalus glycyphyllus*. Perennial herb with zig-zag spreading stems; leaves pinnate, with about 7 pairs of opposite leaflets and an odd one, elliptic; stipules large, free, about ¾ in. long, eared at base on one side; flowers several in axillary long-stalked racemes, greenish-yellow; fruits crowded, slightly bladdery, 1–1¼ in. long, divided lengthwise; seeds kidney-shaped, light yellowish-green.

2 ALPINE ASTRAGALUS, *Astragalus alpinus*. Small herb found only high up in the Scottish Mts.; leaves pinnate with up to 8 pairs of small oblong-elliptic slightly hairy and notched leaflets and a similar end-leaflet; stipules large and leafy, often fringed with dark-coloured hairs; flowers in short long-stalked racemes; calyx 5-lobed, loosely covered with blackish hairs; petals white, tipped with blue; fruits reflexed, 2/3 in. long, loosely hairy with dark hairs.

3 YELLOW OXYTROPIS, *Oxytropis campestris*. Perennial almost stemless herb; lower part covered with remains of stipules and leaf-stalks; leaves pinnate, leaflets 8–12 pairs, oblong-lanceolate, silky-hairy; flowers crowded at the ends of axillary peduncles, pale-yellow tinged with purple; bracts as long as calyx; fruits membranous, about 1 in. long; seeds kidney-shaped, smooth; in rocky places only in Scotland; June, July.

4 BIRD'S-FOOT TREFOIL, *Lotus corniculatus*. Whole summer; widely spread in meadows and pastures; perennial; leaflets 3, with pair of large leafy stipules; flowers 5 or more in umbel; petals yellow, upper (standard) often red on back; pods spirally twisted after opening; red-streaks on back petal guide bees to nectar, effecting cross-pollination by rubbing against the stigma.

14 1 MELILOT, *Melilotus altissima*. Annual or biennial herb up to 4 ft high, easily recognized by the elongated racemes of small yellow flowers which smell like new-mown hay, 3 leaflets, and small transversely nerved fruits which do not open; mostly in waste ground and rubbish dumps, flowering in summer.

2 LUCERNE, *Medicago sativa*. Perennial; stems more or less erect, 1–2 ft long; leaves with 3 leaflets, these oblong-oblanceolate, toothed only towards the apex, the latter sharply apiculate; stipules large, pointed; flowers pale purple, in axillary and terminal racemes; calyx divided to the middle into long slender parts; fruits curved into one or more complete circles, sharply beaked, thinly hairy; valuable fodder plant; naturalized in waste places.

3 SICKLE MEDICK, *Medicago falcata*. Perennial; stems decumbent or rarely erect, 1–2 ft; stipules narrow, undivided; leaflets 3, narrowly obovate to nearly linear; racemes head-like, on axillary peduncles longer than the leaves, yellow, sometimes passing into blue or violet; fruits longer than the calyx, flat, more or less curved but not forming more than one complete ring; dry banks in eastern counties; summer.

4 BLACK MEDICK, NONSUCH, *Medicago lupulina*. Annual with slender mostly procumbent branches up to 2 ft long; stipules large and toothed; leaves with 3 obovate toothed leaflets on a short common stalk; flowers yellow, in small rounded stalked heads in the leaf-axils; fruits crowded into an oblong cluster, very short, curved, black when ripe, reticulate, 1-seeded; a weed in waste places and fields.

5 HOP CLOVER, *Trifolium procumbens*. Slender annual, much branched from the base, procumbent to nearly erect; leaflets 3, obovate, the central one stalked; flowers loose in globose or ovoid heads on rather long axillary peduncles, yellow, fading to pale brown and becoming reflexed; standard petal furrowed lengthwise, concealing the small 1-seeded pod; dry pastures and meadows; spring to autumn.

1 GOLDEN CLOVER, *Trifolium aureum*. Erect or decumbent annual with long branches; leaflets 3, oblanceolate, toothed except at the narrowed base, not hairy; stipules ¾ in. long, narrow, pointed, eared at the base, half as long as leaf-stalk; flowers yellow, in broadly elliptic stalked heads about ¾ in. long in fruit, the persistent petals becoming dry, membranous and striate; naturalized in fields and waste places.

2 CROWN VETCH, *Coronilla varia*. Weak herb; leaves pinnate, with about 6–8 pairs of oblong entire leaflets and a terminal leaflet, the lowermost pair at the base of the common stalk; stipules very small and narrow; flowers clustered at the ends of long axillary peduncles, white, purple or pink; fruits about 8-seeded, breaking up into as many 1-seeded joints; summer.

3 STRAWBERRY CLOVER, *Trifolium fragiferum*. Perennial procumbent herb; leaves with slender stalks; leaflets 3, obovate or elliptic, closely parallel-nerved, margins toothed, about 1 in. long; stipules large, partly united with the stalk; flowers in long-stalked globose heads which soon fruit and form a net-like pinkish ball;

petals pink; fruits enclosed in the inflated calyx; moist meadows and pastures; summer and autumn.

4 HARE'S-FOOT TREFOIL or CLOVER, *Trifolium arvense*. Annual herb with wiry hairy stems; leaves with a very short stalk; leaflets 3, oblanceolate, entire or slightly toothed, hairy below; stipules sharply pointed; flowers very small, white to pale pink, densely crowded into a brush-like spike $\frac{1}{2}$–$\frac{3}{4}$ in. long; fruit a tiny 1-seeded pod embraced by the calyx; dry sandy fields, July to September.

16 1 RED CLOVER, *Trifolium pratense*. Amongst hay and in meadows, an important field crop; perennial up to 2 ft; stipules with sharply pointed lobes; leaflets 3, obovate, nerves numerous, parallel; flowers reddish-purple or rarely white, in dense terminal rounded clusters girt by 2 sessile leaves at base; standard petal like a narrow draining spade; June, July.

2 WHITE or DUTCH CLOVER, *Trifolium repens*. Perennial with numerous spreading stems often rooting at the nodes; stipules inconspicuous; leaflets 3, broadly obovate to rounded, sharply toothed, with a light coloured band across the middle; flowers white or tinged with pink, in globose heads on a long axillary stalk; standard petal with a narrow claw with ridged margins; fruits with 2–4 seeds enclosed in the withered corolla; fields and roadsides.

3 ALSIKE CLOVER, *Trifolium hybridum*. Strong-growing perennial with ascending stems; stipules large, united for $\frac{1}{3}$ their length with the leaf-stalk; leaflets 3, broadly obovate, closely toothed, nerves parallel; flowers at first white, then rose-red, in globose heads about 1 in. diam., standard petal not clawed; fruit with 2–3 seeds; by roadsides.

4 ZIGZAG or MEADOW CLOVER, *Trifolium medium*. Perennial with zigzag branches, finely hairy; leaves rather few and distant, with very large stipules joined to the stalk for nearly half their length; leaflets 3, oblong-oblanceolate, rounded to a short tip, not toothed, with numerous lateral nerves; flowers reddish-purple, in terminal shortly stalked heads; fruits rounded, 1-seeded; open woods, bushy fields and by roadsides.

17 1 REST-HARROW, *Ononis repens*. Spreading herb; branches densely leafy, covered with long weak whitish, several-celled hairs; leaflet 1, with a large leafy stipule adnate to the short stalk, sharply toothed,

18

covered with sticky glandular hairs; flowers axillary, solitary, pink, the standard streaked with deeper shade; fruit about as long as calyx, 2–3-seeded; in grassy places and sand-dunes; summer and autumn.

2 HAIRY GENISTA, *Genista pilosa*. Stems prostrate, with numerous short hard branches; no thorns; leaves simple, obovate, hairless above but covered below with short silky hairs; flowers axillary, shortly stalked; petals yellow, silky-hairy outside; stamens all united into one sheath; fruits hairy, flattened; rare; spring and early summer.

3 PETTY WHIN, NEEDLE FURZE, *Genista anglica*. A tiny very thorny shrublet; young leafy shoots produced below the spines; leaves small, simple, obovate; flowers yellow, about ½ in. long; stamens 10, united into a single tube, anthers alternately short and attached in the middle, and long and attached at the base; fruits inflated like short broad pea-pods; seeds rounded, dark brown; on heaths and moors; spring and early summer.

4 BROOM, *Cytisus scoparius*. Shrub up to 5 ft; branches straight and whip-like, angular; leaves divided into 3 small leaflets; flowers in leafy racemes, bright yellow; stamens all united into a tube, 5 long and 5 shorter; fruits compressed, hairy on the margins; seeds with large fleshy aril at base; branches used for basket work; broom-tops used in medicine.

5 KIDNEY VETCH, LADY'S FINGERS, *Anthyllis vulneraria*. A handsome perennial herb; stems up to about 1½ ft; leaves pinnate, sessile, leaflets narrow; flower-heads up to 1½ in. diam., girt by narrow leafy bracts; flowers yellow varying to deep red; standard petal spoon-shaped; stamens united into one sheath, anthers equal; most abundant on chalky soils; early summer.

1 IVY, *Hedera helix*. Late summer and autumn; creeping or climb- **18** ing shrub with sucker-like aerial outgrowths; leaves evergreen, those of the flowering shoots less lobed and often entire; flowers yellowish green; petals free; fruit a berry providing food for birds, especially pigeons; the last wild climber to flower in Britain; insects effect cross-pollination by crawling over the platform of flowers.

2 DWARF CORNEL, *Chamaepericlymenum suecicum*. June–July; perennial herb with creeping rootstock; stems to 6 in. high; leaves opposite, sessile, parallel nerved lengthwise, with scattered T-

shaped hairs above; flowers very small in a terminal cluster surrounded by 4 large yellowish-white bracts resembling large petals; petals 4, free, dark purple; only found in hills and mountains in the north, with circumpolar distribution; fruit a bunch of red berries.

3 DOGWOOD, *Cornus sanguinea*. June–July; shrub up to 6 ft; leaves opposite, pinnately nerved, no stipules, thinly clothed below with T-shaped hairs; flowers in a terminal lax cluster (cymes); no bracts; petals 4, dull white, free; stamens 4, alternate with petals; ovary inferior; common in hedges and copses on chalky downs in the south, rare in the north; annual shoots used for baskets.

19 1 NORWAY MAPLE, *Acer platanoides*. Tree up to 90 ft high, with large spreading crown; leaves orbicular in outline, about 6 in. diam., 5-lobed, lobes with a few large teeth, nerves radiating from the base, with small tufts of hairs in the axils; flowers yellowish green, in small cymes appearing with the young leaves; stalks slender; fruits with 2 widely spreading lobes about $1\frac{3}{4}$ in. long, winged on the upper side; introduced and naturalized and found in woods, hedges and plantations.

2 SPINDLE TREE, *Euonymus europaeus*. Shrub to about 6 ft high; leaves deciduous, opposite, at length about 3 in. long and $1\frac{1}{2}$ in. broad, elliptic, slightly toothed; flowers in little axillary stalked cymes, the middle flower opening first; sepals 4; petals 4, yellowish green; stamens 4; fruits 4-lobed, red to pink, opening into the lobes; seeds covered by a fleshy aril; poisonous in all its parts.

3 ALDER BUCKTHORN, BLACK ALDER, *Frangula alnus*. Shrub; branches alternate, without thorns; leaves alternate, broadly elliptic to obovate, entire; flowers several in each leaf-axil; sepals 5; petals 5, small and narrow, each embracing a very short stamen; fruit globose, black when ripe, about $\frac{1}{4}$ in. diam.; spring and early summer.

4 BUCKTHORN, *Rhamnus catharticus*. Shrub, branchlets thorny; leaves deciduous, clustered, elliptic or ovate-elliptic, shortly toothed; flowers green, of one sex, males on one bush, females on another; sepals 4; petals 4, small and narrow, each embracing a stamen, stamens longer than the petals; fruit globose, black when ripe, about $\frac{1}{4}$ in. diam.; wood makes gunpowder and charcoal, and the berries (poisonous) sap green for water colours; spring and early summer.

1 BAY WILLOW, *Salix pentandra*. Tree up to 40 ft, or large shrub; winter-buds sharply keeled, shining; leaves fragrant when bruised, elliptic, sharply pointed, about 4 in. long and 1½ in. broad, not hairy, toothed, with about 10 pairs of lateral nerves; catkins appearing with or just after the leaves, males about 1½ in. long; stamens usually about 5; on river banks and marshy places; spring.

2 CRACK WILLOW, *Salix fragilis*. Bushy tree; mature leaves on fairly long stalks, broadly oblong, taper-pointed, rather coarsely toothed on the margins, hairless on both surfaces, lateral nerves numerous; flowers developed with the leaves, catkins very slender on short leafy shoots; stamens 2; spring.

3 OSIER, *Salix viminalis*. Shrub or tree up to 30 ft, with slender branches; leaves produced after flowering, linear to very narrowly linear-lanceolate, acutely acuminate, hairless above, softly silvery-silky below; lateral nerves very numerous, arched; stipules linear; catkins about 1 in. long; stamens 2; cultivated for its long pliant shoots for basket-making; spring.

4 GREAT SALLOW WILLOW, *Salix caprea*. Tall shrub or bushy tree; leaves broadly elliptic or obovate-elliptic, shortly pointed, crenate, wrinkled, cottony-hairy below; catkins short and thick; male floral bracts with a fringe of long hairs at the top; stamens 2, anthers long-exserted; fruit silky; woods and copses, making good fences, hurdles, and as soil-binder; spring.

1 WOOLLY WILLOW, *Salix lanata*. Much branched shrublet up to 2 ft high; leaves ovate, thickly woolly on both surfaces; catkins covered with dense long silky hairs of a fine golden yellow, in the fruiting stage nearly 3 in. long; capsules cottony-hairy, tapered to the apex, ¼ in. long; Scotland only; early summer.

2 CREEPING WILLOW, *Salix repens*. Low straggling shrublet with decumbent branches rooting at lower nodes; mature leaves elliptic, about 1 in. long, grey-silky below with appressed hairs; male catkins about ½ in. long; stamens 2, anthers on long slender filaments; female catkins about 1 in. long in fruit; fruits splitting into 2 recurved halves, hairy; on heaths, moors and in sandy places; spring.

3 DWARF WILLOW, *Salix herbacea*. Small shrublet with half-underground stems creeping and rooting; branches about 2 in. above ground; leaves obovate to orbicular, ½ in. long, crenate,

green and hairless, veiny, sometimes slightly hairy when young; catkins ovoid, few-flowered, on short leafless peduncles opposite the last leaf of the young shoots; capsules nearly hairless; northern Britain and Eire; summer.

4 RETICULATE WILLOW, *Salix reticulata*. Habit like the above, branches up to 6 in. high, sometimes hairy when young; leaves obovate to orbicular, not toothed, ¾–1 in. long, green hairless and wrinkled above, white below; catkins on rather long leafless peduncles opposite the last leaf, both sexes cylindric, ½–1 in. long, shortly hairy; capsules cottony-hairy; high up on Scottish mountains; summer.

22 1 ALDER, *Alnus glutinosa*. Moderate-sized tree with dark foliage, flowering in early spring before the leaves, the catkins formed in previous autumn; bark at length brownish black; leaves obovate, rounded to wedge-shaped at the base, widely notched at the apex, toothed in the upper part; stipules soon falling off; flowers of one sex, males in pendulous catkins; female catkins very short and ellipsoid, cone-like; pollination by wind.

2 GREY ALDER, *Alnus incana*. A tree up to 70 ft high; bark smooth, silvery grey; leaves ovate or oval, rounded or wedge-shaped at the base, acute or slightly acuminate, lobulate-toothed; lower surface greyish, covered with soft hairs; stipules soon falling off; male catkins as in *A. glutinosa* but looser, with red-brown seeds and yellow anthers; in Britain only in cultivation in woods.

23 1 DWARF BIRCH, *Betula nana*. A small shrub or very small tree; leaves very small, orbicular, serrate-crenate, about ½ in. long and broad, prominently net-veined below; catkins small and sessile, males oblong, the females scarcely ¼ in. long but about ½ in. long in fruit; scales 3-lobed, with nearly equal lobes; on moors and in bogs in northern Britain; May.

2 BOG MYRTLE, *Myrica gale*. Small shrub up to 3–4 ft often common in boggy acid soils; stems purplish; leaves produced after flowering, oblanceolate, toothed, gland-dotted below and very aromatic when bruised; male-spikes catkin-like but stiff, females shorter on separate plants; no sepals or petals; fruit small, winged, glandular; pollen distributed by the wind.

3 ASPEN, *Populus tremula*. A large tree with long-stalked suborbicular toothed leaves which tremble in the slightest breeze;

leaves tomentose when young, soon hairless and pale or glaucous beneath; glands at base 2, cup-shaped, well developed on terminal leaves of long vigorous shoots; catkins subsessile, densely and greyish tomentose; scales fringed with long white hairs.

1 WYCH ELM, *Ulmus glabra*. Large tree up to 120 ft high, often **24** branched from the base; young branchlets roughly hairy; winterbuds with rust-coloured hairs on the scales; leaves large, 6–18 cm., suborbicular to elliptic, long-pointed, rough above, hairy below, auriculate on one side at the base and overlapping the short stalk; February, March; in woods and by streams.

2 BIRCH, *Betula verrucosa*. Tree up to 90 ft high; branchlets and leaves hairless; leaves deltoid with a broad cuneate base and acuminate apex, doubly serrate; fruiting catkins cylindrical about 1 in. long, on slender glandular stalk about ½ in. long; scales ciliate, with rounded recurved lateral lobes larger than the middle lobe; spring.

3 BIRCH, *Betula pubescens*. Graceful tree with pale smooth bark; young and two-year-old shoots densely covered with short soft hairs; leaves ovate, toothed but not lobulate, more or less hairy below, especially in the axils of the nerves; fruiting catkins cylindrical, about 1 in. long, on a long pubescent stalk; scales ciliate, with the central lobe longer than in *B. verrucosa*; spring.

1 HORNBEAM, *Carpinus betulus*. A tree up to 90 ft with the hardest, **25** heaviest, and toughest wood of our native kinds; leaves deciduous, elliptic, doubly serrate, pale green below with hairs on the nerves and in their axils; flowers appearing with the young leaves, of one sex, the males in pendulous catkins about 1¼ in. long, female about 1 in. long; fruits amongst overlapping leafy enlarged bracts.

2 HAZEL-NUT, *Corylus avellana*. Shrub or small branched tree, young shoots with gland-tipped hairs; leaves deciduous, ovate-orbicular, cordate, doubly toothed; male flowers in slender pendulous catkins, in very early spring, females in a sessile scaly cluster from which protrude the red stigmas; fruits solitary or clustered; branches used for walking-sticks, hurdles, crates, and interlaced fencing.

1 BEECH, *Fagus sylvatica*. Large tree with thick smooth trunk and **26** dense crown with lovely young foliage in spring; wood hard, a valuable timber; leaves deciduous, ovate-elliptic, soft and silky

when young; flowers produced with the leaves, of one sex, the males in globular pendulous stalked clusters, females clustered on a short erect stalk; fruits a favourite food for pigs.

2 PEDUNCULATE OAK, *Quercus robur*. There are two native oaks in Britain, that shown here with shortly stalked leaves ear-shaped at the base, hairless below, and the acorns borne on a slender common stalk; and the second species, *Q. petraea*, the Sessile Oak, the leaves of which have fairly long stalks, wedge-shaped at base, hairy beneath, and acorns sessile or nearly so; male flowers in catkins, in spring.

27 1 SUN SPURGE, *Euphorbia helioscopia*. Annual up to 2½ ft, with milky juice; leaves spirally arranged, few and scattered, broadly spoon-shaped, glaucous-green, slightly toothed; upper 5 leaves in a whorl and forming a ring of bracts similar to leaves but broader and rounded at the base; stalks of flower-clusters 5, with 3 bracts below the flowers; fruits 3-lobed; seeds reticulate; fields and waste places.

2 DOG'S MERCURY, *Mercurialis perennis*. Perennial, in woods and shady places, flowering in early spring; leaves opposite, elliptic to oblong-lanceolate, toothed; flowers of one sex, male and female on separate plants, in slender axillary inflorescences; calyx 2–3-lobed; no petals; fruit a 2-lobed capsule, bristly-hairy; seeds warted; poisonous to stock.

3 STINGING NETTLE, *Urtica dioica*. Strong-growing perennial easily determined by the sharp stinging hairs; leaves opposite, stalked, ovate-cordate, coarsely toothed; flowers of one sex, usually on separate plants, clustered in axillary panicles, male flowers green; stamens 4; ovary with a tufted stigma; fruit a flattened seed-like nut enclosed in the calyx; a noxious weed, but leaves valued as a source of chlorophyll; stem fibrous.

4 SMALL STINGING NETTLE, *Urtica urens*. Erect annual covered with stiff stinging hairs; leaves opposite, ovate or elliptic, coarsely toothed, 3-nerved from the base; male and female flowers intermixed on the same plant, in loose axillary clusters; stamens 4; ovary with a tufted stigma; fruit a small nutlet with 1 seed; waste and cultivated places, often a garden weed.

5 HOP, *Humulus lupulus*. Perennial herb with a thick branched rootstock; stems annual, twining to a considerable height over other plants and on hedges; leaves opposite, stalked, deeply heart-

shaped at the base, the larger deeply 3–5-lobed and sharply toothed, smaller less divided or only toothed; flowers of one sex, males in loose panicles with small bracts, females in ovoid heads covered with green overlapping bracts; much cultivated in Kent and Worcestershire for brewing purposes.

1 CREEPING ST JOHN'S WORT, *Hypericum humifusum*; decum- **28** bent perennial herb, sometimes forming dense spreading tufts; leaves sessile, opposite, broadly elliptic, pale green, hairless, gland-dotted and with a few black glands; flowers few; petals 5, free, rich-cream-yellow with streaks of red outside; stamens about 15, in 3 bundles; styles 3; capsule wrapped in the dry persistent sepals and petals; in various habitats; early summer to autumn.

2 MARSH VIOLET, *Viola palustris*. Found in spongy bogs and swampy places in woods, common in Scotland and Eire, but less so in England and Wales; perennial herb with a creeping root-stock and a tangle of fine roots; leaf-blade almost orbicular except the deeply cordate base, about 1½–2 in. diam., hairless; bracts 2 below the middle of the flower-stalks; petals pale blue with purple streaks, spur short and very broad; spring, early summer.

3 SUNDEW, *Drosera rotundifolia*. Herb often very common in boggy acid soil amongst Sphagnum moss; leaves in a rosette, long-stalked, spoon-shaped or rounded, covered above with sticky-tipped processes which entrap small insects; flowering stem often forked, the white flowers borne to one side; summer.

4 ROCK ROSE, *Helianthemum chamaecistus*. All summer; much branched shrublet, partial to limestone and chalk; leaves opposite, oblong-lanceolate to almost ovate, green above, hoary or white beneath with branched hairs; small stipules; flowers bright yellow or rarely white, in a terminal raceme; stamens numerous; ovary 1-locular, with ovules on the walls; flowers close at night and in wet weather.

1 IMPERFORATE ST JOHN'S WORT, *Hypericum dubium*. Perennial **29** herb from a rhizome; stems 4-sided but not winged; leaves sessile, elliptic, contracted at the base, usually without glandular dots; flowers golden yellow, about ¾ in. diam.; sepals entire, glandular; petals margined with black dots; stamens in bundles; margins of woods and hedgebanks; June–August.

2 UPRIGHT ST JOHN'S WORT, *Hypericum pulchrum*. Found in dry woods, open heaths and waste land, flowering summer; perennial with slender rounded stems; leaves opposite, sessile, ovate, cordate at the base, $\frac{1}{2}$–$\frac{3}{4}$ in. long, with transparent glands towards the margin; flowers rather few in loose oblong cymes; petals yellow, about $\frac{1}{2}$ in. long, margined with sessile black glands; summer.

3 MALLOW, *Malva sylvestris*. Erect biennial or perennial herb; stems, leaf-stalks and flower-stalks clothed with long spreading hairs with swollen bases; leaves alternate, on long stalks, 3–7-lobed, often 5-lobed, to about the middle; stipules large and pointed; flowers clustered, pale reddish-purple or blue, marked with darker circles; fruit of about 10 carpels, flat and disk-like; from mid-June.

4 DWARF MALLOW, *Malva neglecta*. Procumbent annual of roadsides and waste-places; leaves long-stalked, orbicular, deeply cordate at base, slightly 5–7-lobed; stipules lanceolate; flowers clustered in leaf-axils, pale blue, about 1 in. diam.; carpels 10–15 forming a hairy disk-like fruit with the persistent sepals like a rosette; spring to autumn.

30 1 SWEET VIOLET, *Viola odorata*. Perennial herb with numerous runners; leaves on long stalks, ovate to almost orbicular, widely cordate at the base, averaging $1\frac{1}{4}$–$1\frac{3}{4}$ in. long (larger in shade), crenate, very shortly hairy; stipules finely toothed; flowers sweetly scented, on stalks mostly exceeding the leaves with a pair of opposite bracts half way up; petals bluish-purple, often white, lowermost with a blunt round spur at base; early spring.

2 HAIRY VIOLET, *Viola hirta*. Leaves and leaf-stalks thinly hairy all over; leaves very similar to those of the Dog Violet (below) but larger, up to $2\frac{1}{2}$ in. long and $1\frac{1}{2}$ in. broad; stipules toothed; flowers not scented, with 2 bracts near the middle; petals bluish-purple, the spur short and thick, straight; chiefly in rocky places, open woods and fields, mainly in limestone, flowering later than the Sweet Violet (above).

3 WOOD VIOLET, *Viola riviniana*. Perennial herb; leaves as above, not hairy but closely gland-dotted on both surfaces; stipules with long comb-like teeth on the margin; flowers on long stalks with a pair of narrow bracts about 1 in. below the flower; sepals produced below the point of attachments; petals blue, the lowest produced into a large blunt grooved spur; in woods; spring.

4 DOG VIOLET, *Viola canina*. Perennial herb; leaves long-stalked, ovate, cordate at base, about 1 in. long and broad, minutely hairy on upper surface, green or finely mottled below, crenulate; stipules linear; flowers not scented, on rather long stalks with 2 linear bracts towards the top; petals pale purplish-blue, sometimes white, prominently nerved; front petal spurred; common; spring and early summer.

1 SHEPHERD'S PURSE, *Capsella bursa-pastoris*. Common annual weed in gardens, fields, and waste ground, flowering nearly all the year round, clothed with stellate hairs; leaves in a rosette, entire or pinnately lobed; lower stem-leaves narrowed to the base, upper clasping the stem with ear-like base; flowers white, very small; fruits narrowly obtriangular, shortly 2-lobed at top.

2 SCURVY GRASS, *Cochlearia officinalis*. Fleshy seaside annual or biennial up to 1 ft, well known to sailors in olden times as a remedy for scurvy; lower leaves long-stalked, rounded-ovate, widely cordate at base, sometimes larger and pentagonal; stem-leaves sessile and eared at the base; flowers white, in short racemes; fruits broadly ellipsoid, $\frac{1}{4}$ in. long, reticulate; seeds curved, closely pitted; summer.

3 WHITLOW GRASS, *Erophila verna*. Dwarf early spring annual; leaves in a dense rosette, spreading, oblanceolate to ovate, slightly toothed, clothed with star-shaped hairs; flowering stems several; flowers very small, white; fruits on long slender stalks, about $\frac{1}{4}$ in. long, compressed, containing numerous minute seeds.

4 HEARTSEASE, *Viola tricolor*. April to October; often common in cultivated ground, rarely in pastures or river shingles; a real wild Pansy; annual, with much divided stipules and long-stalked spoon-shaped crenate leaves; flowers variable in colour, usually a mixture of purple, white and yellow, often the upper petals tinged or tipped with purple; lower petal spurred at the base; seeds like little brown eggs.

5 FIELD PANSY, *Viola arvensis*. A slender annual with stems up to 1 ft, with narrower leaves and lobes of stipules than in Heartsease; petals also much smaller, often shorter than the sepals, pale yellow or nearly white, or the upper ones pale purple; a common weed in fields and gardens, by some considered to be a variety or form of Heartsease.

32 1 SMALL ALISON, *Alyssum alyssoides*. Annual herb, covered all over with whitish stellate hairs; lower part of stem leafless; leaves alternate, linear-oblanceolate, 1-nerved; flowers in terminal racemes; petals very narrow, yellow; contracted above the middle; fruits compressed, orbicular, covered with short stellate hairs and with 2 seeds in each division; seeds winged; in fields and arable land; spring, early summer.

2 HOARY BERTEROA, *Berteroa incana*. Erect annual herb clothed all over with stellate hairs; stem-leaves sessile, narrowly lanceolate, grey-green, entire, about 2 in. long; flowers racemose-corymbose, covered with stalked stellate hairs, one arm longer than the others; petals white, deeply bilobed; fruit oblong, compressed, covered with short stellate hairs; seeds compressed, finely warted; dry places along railways and roadsides; summer.

3 FIELD PENNY CRESS, *Thlaspi arvense*. Erect hairless annual up to about 1 ft, the white flowers rapidly developing into fruits in an elongated raceme; upper leaves sessile and ear-shaped at the base, oblong, toothed; fruits orbicular, thin and flat, not quite as big as a farthing, broadly winged and deeply notched at the top; seeds lined by several ribs; a weed in waste places; spring, summer.

4 ALPINE PENNY CRESS, *Thlaspi alpestre*. Biennial or perennial herb forming clumps; basal leaves long-stalked, spoon-shaped-obovate, about 1 in. long, hairless; stem-leaves few, sessile, rather cordate at base; flowers numerous in racemes; fruits winged at the top, wings forming a wide notch, the valves falling away from the partition; mountain pastures in limestone districts; summer.

5 NARROW-LEAVED CRESS, *Lepidium ruderale*. Hairless annual, up to 1 ft high, with much branched wiry stems; basal and lower leaves deeply pinnately lobed, lobes narrow, upper leaves entire or nearly so and linear; flowers very small, whitish, usually without petals; stamens 2; fruits small, rounded, valves keeled or slightly winged at the apex; style minute; mostly near the sea in the southern counties of England; early summer.

33 1 ALPINE ROCKCRESS, *Arabis alpina*. A very rare rock plant found in Britain only in the island of Skye; low spreading perennial with decumbent stems; basal leaves spoon-shaped, coarsely toothed, densely covered with stalked branched hairs; flowering-stem-leaves eared at the base, sessile; flowers white; fruits slender and undulate, $1\frac{1}{2}$ in. long.

2 SEA KALE, *Crambe maritima*. Perennial with fleshy roots on sandy and shingly sea-coasts; leaves large and thick, up to nearly a foot long, ovate-triangular in outline but margins wavy and irregularly toothed, very glaucous; flowers in a panicle of racemes, white; petals 4; stamens 6; stigma sessile; fruit ellipsoid, reticulate, 1-seeded.

3 WALL CRESS, *Arabidopsis thaliana*. Slender erect annual; leaves in a basal rosette, narrow, toothed, sprinkled on both surfaces with stiff simple or 2–3-armed hairs; stem-leaves few and sessile; flowers white, at first in a bunch, at length the main axis elongated in fruit; fruits about ¾ in. long, on spreading stalks, 1-nerved; seeds numerous, very small, rounded; in light sandy fields, on walls and rocks; early spring.

4 TOWER MUSTARD, *Turritis glabra*. Erect biennial with basal rosette of leaves which wither during the fruiting period; leaves like those of a Dandelion but clothed with scattered forked hairs; stem-leaves sessile, markedly eared at the base, entire; flowers yellowish or greenish white, in short racemes; fruits 2½ in. long, erect, with a nerve up the middle of each valve; seeds compressed, margined; May to June.

1 SEA ROCKET, *Cakile maritima*. Leaves fleshy, deeply lobed; fruits 34 very distinctive, with a short thick stalk, at first narrow, when ripe separating transversely into 2 parts, upper half falling away with 1 erect seed, lower half persistent; fleshy annual near the sea and salt marshes; flowers pale mauve, veiny, in short leaf-opposed racemes; June to autumn.

2 GARLIC MUSTARD, *Alliaria officinalis*. Erect annual or biennial, in colonies under hedges and in shady waste places; when rubbed giving off strong smell like garlic; lower leaves on long stalks, ovate-triangular, widely cordate at base, coarsely toothed; nerves spreading from the base; flowers white, in small clusters which elongate in fruit; fruits spreading, about 2 in. long, nearly cylindrical; seeds lined lengthwise; spring.

3 CUCKOO FLOWER, LADY'S SMOCK, *Cardamine pratensis*. Perennial, scattered or in colonies in moist meadows and by sides of streams; leaves pinnate; flowers at first corymbose, white to mauve; fruits about 1 in. long; seeds in a single row in each partition; one of our first spring flowers along with the Primrose.

4 MARSH WATERCRESS, *Rorippa islandica*. Annual or biennial herb

in moist places; tap-root pale and slender; stem angular; lower leaves deeply pinnately lobed, the end-lobe the largest and toothed; upper leaves becoming sessile, eared at the base; flowers yellow, very small in lax racemes and soon producing fruit; petals scarcely exceeding the sepals; fruits oblong, turgid, curved, about as long as the stalk; summer, autumn.

35 1 HEDGE MUSTARD, *Sisymbrium officinale*. Erect tough annual up up 1½ ft, becoming zigzag with age; lower leaves deeply and very irregularly pinnately lobed, lobes unequally toothed, thinly bristly on both surfaces; flowers very small, yellow, at first in short racemes which greatly elongate in fruit; fruits remaining parallel with the axis, about ½ in. long, pointed, valves with a keel-like midrib; seeds with a flat end; weed; summer.

  2 FLIXWEED, *Sisymbrium sophia*. Erect annual up to 2½ ft; stems with minute stellate hairs; leaves 2–3 times pinnate from the base, up to about 3 in. long, segments narrow; flowers yellow, very small, in terminal racemes which elongate in fruit to 1 ft; petals spoon-shaped, shorter than sepals; fruits ¾ in. long, slightly curved and wavy with a distinct midrib down the middle of the valves; waste places and sandy fields; summer.

  3 WINTERCRESS, *Barbarea vulgaris*. Perennial often in clumps, up to 2½ ft; lower stem-leaves deeply pinnately divided, terminal lobe largest; upper stem-leaves sessile and markedly eared at base, lobed or toothed; racemes forming a panicle; sepals hairless, outer horned at apex; petals yellow; fruits very narrow, wavy, erect, about 1 in. long, beaked; seeds pitted; roadsides, hedgebanks and by canals; spring and summer.

  4 EASTERN BUNIAS, *Bunias orientalis*. Herb, usually biennial, up to 4 ft; root carrot-shaped; stem glandular above; basal leaves lyrately lobed, with stellate hairs on both surfaces, upper leaves sessile, narrow, with scattered glands on margins; flowers bright yellow, in lax panicles; fruits short and ovoid, often obliquely constricted in the middle, beaked, veiny and glandular; seeds 2; cultivated land and river banks.

36 1 TURNIP, *Brassica rapa*. Annual or biennial herb, with turnip root; stems up to 3 ft; basal leaves stalked, lyrately lobulate, bristly; stem-leaves sessile, clasping the stem, glaucous, cordate at the base; open flowers often overtopping the buds, bright yellow;

outer stamens very short; fruit rather flattened, tapered into a beak; seeds blackish or reddish brown.

2 CHARLOCK, WILD MUSTARD, *Sinapis arvensis*. Usually a wide expanse of bright yellow amongst the corn in summer; annual; stems with a few stiff whitish hairs; upper leaves sessile, coarsely toothed, with stiff hairs on nerves; fruits soon developed, about 1½ in. long, upper part beaked, lower part smooth or with stiff reflexed hairs containing about a dozen black seeds; a troublesome weed.

3 WILD RADISH, *Raphanus raphanistrum*. Annual or biennial up to 2 ft; stems with stiff spreading bristly hairs; leaves deeply pinnately lobed, terminal lobe much the largest, obovate-rounded, other lobes small and spreading, bristly hairy; flowers few in a terminal raceme, showy, either white with coloured veins or pale yellow or lilac; fruits with a long beak, contracted between the 4–7 seeds (or 1–2-seeded); seeds reticulate; summer and autumn.

4 TREACLE MUSTARD, *Erysimum cheiranthoides*. Erect annual to 2½ ft, clothed with medifixed hairs; leaves lanceolate, slightly toothed; flowers pale yellow, numerous in panicles of racemes; fruits ribbed-angular, ¾ in. long, shortly beaked; seeds smooth and brown; in cultivated and waste ground; summer and autumn; seeds formerly used in rustic medicines.

1 MARSH ANDROMEDA, *Andromeda polifolia*. Shrublet up to 1 ft; 37 leaves evergreen, alternate, oblanceolate, up to 1¼ in. long, dark green and shining above, very glaucous below and densely papillous, with distinct spreading lateral nerves, margins strongly recurved; flowers in a terminal bunch; calyx deeply 5-lobed; corolla pale pink, ovoid-globular; 5 short recurved lobes; stamens 10, included; anthers with 2 long curved horns at the top; in peat-bogs; summer.

2 STRAWBERRY TREE, *Arbutus unedo*. Small tree or shrub, found wild only in south-west Eire, flowering in autumn; to be seen in some botanic gardens; leaves evergreen, ovate-elliptic to oblong, toothed, thick, shining above; flowers greenish-white in drooping panicles; corolla bell-shaped, shortly 5-lobed; stamens 10, anthers opening by terminal pores, with 2 horn-like appendages.

3 BELL HEATHER, *Erica cinerea*. Woody shrublet; leaves 3 in a whorl, often with short hairs in their axils, short and needle-like, acute, margins recurved and meeting together below; flowers in

interrupted clusters on short shoots; corolla reddish-purple, with 4 very short lobes; stamens 8, anthers opening by pores with 2 toothed appendages at the base; moorlands, in company with common Heather; summer and autumn.

4 BLUE PHYLLODOCE, *Phyllodoce caerulea*. Small wiry shrublet, densely leafy; leaves alternate, shortly linear, about $\frac{1}{2}$ in. long, 1-nerved, finely toothed; flowers pink to purplish-blue, clustered in an umbel-like inflorescence; pedicels $1-1\frac{1}{2}$ in. long, crimson and shortly glandular; calyx deeply 5-lobed; corolla bell-shaped, 5-toothed; stamens 10, free; anthers opening by 2 terminal pores, without appendages; only in Scotland.

5 TRAILING LOISELEURIA, 'AZALEA', *Loiseleuria procumbens*. Shrublet with procumbent stems; leaves evergreen, opposite, crowded, tapered to a thick stalk, a prominent thick midrib below, margins thick and strongly recurved, hairy between the midrib and margin; flowers few at the ends of the branches; calyx deeply 5-lobed; corolla rose-pink, 5-lobed to the middle; stamens 5, on the disk; fruit a red capsule; forms dense carpets on moors only in Scotland.

38 1 RED BEARBERRY, *Arctostaphylos uva-ursi*. Low shrub; winter bud-scales persistent; leaves evergreen, oblanceolate, about 1 in. long, shining on both surfaces, margins covered with short hairs when young; flowers drooping in short terminal racemes; sepals 5, rounded; corolla ovoid, shortly 5-lobed; stamens 10; anthers opening by pores; fruit globose, red, glossy.

2 BLACK or ALPINE BEARBERRY, *Arctostaphylos alpina*. Prostrate shrublet; leaves deciduous, obovate, serrulate, ciliate; flowers few in terminal clusters; sepals 5, triangular; corolla urceolate, shortly 5-lobed; stamens 10; anthers opening by pores; fruit globose; bluish-black; only in Scotland; May to August.

3 CROSS-LEAVED HEATH, *Erica tetralix*. Low shrublet; leaves in whorls of 4, margins much recurved, markedly papillous below, also with long stiff hairs near the margin; sepals oblong, with a few bristles; corolla tubular, 4-lobed; stamens 8; anthers with 2 long appendages at base, opening by terminal pores; grows with Heather (below), less abundant; late summer; a bee plant.

4 SCOTCH HEATHER, LING, *Calluna vulgaris*. Shrublet up to 2 ft or more but often dwarfer; branches softly hairy; leaves opposite, in 4 rows, very small, produced below the point of attachment;

flowers very small in leafy racemes, pink or rarely white; corolla shorter than calyx, deeply 4-lobed; stamens 8; anthers with 2 tails at base, opening by long pore-like slits; dominant on moors with acid soil, July to early September; valuable bee-plant.

1 PONTUS RHODODENDRON, *Rhododendron ponticum*. Large
shrub naturalized and planted in woodlands; native of Asia Minor; leaves falsely whorled, oblanceolate, hairless; flowers in a terminal cluster surrounded by numerous ovate pointed winter-bud scales which soon fall away; calyx a mere rim; corolla widely funnel-shaped, deeply 5-lobed, purple, spotted at back with brownish streaks; stamens 10, slightly hairy; anthers opening by terminal pores; style curved, crimson; late spring.

2 MARSH LEDUM, *Ledum palustre*. Small erect shrub; branchlets densely hairy; leaves alternate, broadly and shortly linear; gland-ular above, densely rusty-hairy below, margins much recurved; flowers white, in a terminal umbel-like raceme from a scaly winter-bud; calyx very small; petals 5, free; stamens 10; anthers opening by 2 terminal pores; seeds tailed at each end; boggy swamps in Scotland, perhaps not native.

3 YELLOW BIRD'S-NEST, *Monotropa hypopitys*. Saprophyte associated with mycorhiza on roots of trees, beech, pines, and willows; stem up to 9 in.; leaves scale-like, yellow; flowers pale yellow, in a terminal bracteate raceme; sepals and petals 5 or 4 each, latter free; stamens as many as petals; ovary deeply 4-5-lobed; seeds tailed at each end; summer.

4 CROWBERRY, *Empetrum nigrum*. Low shrublet; older branches rough with persistent leaf-bases; leaves crowded, evergreen, about $\frac{1}{4}$ in. long, flat on top, edges rolled back showing only midrib below; flowers axillary, sessile; sepals 3; petals 3, free; stamens 3-4, alternate with the petals; ovary superior, globose, 3-9-locular; stigmas 6 or more; fruit a small black berry; on mountain heaths and in bogs especially northern Britain; May-June.

1 LARGER WINTERGREEN, *Pyrola rotundifolia*. Perennial herb with
slender creeping rootstock; leaves towards the base of the stem, long-stalked, like broad spoons, entire or slightly toothed, 1-2 in. long, hairless; flowers drooping; sepals 5, narrow; corolla-lobes 5, white, free nearly to the base; stamens 10; anthers opening by

terminal pores; style longer than corolla; seeds minute, tailed at each end; rare; summer.

2 SMALL WINTERGREEN, *Pyrola minor*. Very similar to the Larger Wintergreen (above) but much smaller, the petals quite free to the base, and the style shorter than the petals and fruit; frequent in Scotland and northern England, local in other parts and in Eire; summer.

3 SERRATED WINTERGREEN, *Pyrola secunda*. Perennial about 6 in. high; leaves stalked, ovate, acute, serrulate; flowers to one side in a raceme, the common stalk with a few scattered bracts; petals 5, free, greenish-white, erect or incurved; stamens 10, anthers opening by pores; style longer than the ovary and fruit; capsule drooping; from mountains of Wales to Scotland; July–August.

4 ONE-FLOWERED WINTERGREEN, *Moneses uniflora*. Perennial herb with slender creeping rootstock; leaves in whorls of 3 or 4, stalked, rounded, crenate, hairless; flowers single on a long stalk, drooping; petals 5, white, slightly united at the base; stamens 10, with large anthers opening by pores; capsule globular, opening by slits down the middle of the loculi; seeds elongated, reticulate; very rare, only in Scotland; June–July.

5 LAPLAND DIAPENSIA, *Diapensia lapponica*. Densely tufted woody perennial forming small clumps; leaves in rosettes, spoon-shaped, hairless; flowers single in the middle of each rosette of leaves; stalks bracteate; sepals 5, free; corolla white, broadly tubular, 5-lobed nearly to middle; stamens 5, between lobes; anthers cordate, no appendages; ovary superior, 3-locular; fruit a capsule; quite recently discovered in Scotland, very rare; June–July.

41 1 BILBERRY, BLUEBERRY, WHORTLEBERRY, *Vaccinium myrtillus*. Shrublet about 1 ft high; branchlets flattened or almost winged; leaves deciduous, alternate, ovate-elliptic, minutely toothed; flowers solitary, axillary, pendulous; calyx united with the inferior ovary, a mere rim; corolla globose, shortly lobed, greenish tinged with red; stamens twice as many as lobes, anthers with 2 long horns; on mountain and hilly heaths and woods; berries grouse food, and for tarts and jam.

2 BOG WHORTLEBERRY, *Vaccinium uliginosum*. Shrublet about 1–2 ft high, with leafy twigs; branchlets not winged; leaves

34

deciduous, alternate, rounded-obovate, coarsely net-veined below; flowers solitary, axillary, pendulous; calyx united with the inferior ovary, lobes ovate; corolla ellipsoid, shortly lobed, pale pink, lobes short and reflexed; fruit globose, black with a glaucous bloom; only in northern Britain; May–June.

3 RED WHORTLEBERRY, COWBERRY, *Vaccinium vitis-idaea*. Shrublet with wiry procumbent stems rooting at the base; leaves evergreen, alternate, obovate, slightly dentate; flowers in a short terminal curved or drooping bracteate raceme; calyx of 4 ovate sepals borne on top of inferior ovary; corolla white or pale rose, 4-lobed; stamens 8; anthers prolonged into long tubes at the apex with a hole at top; on moors and heaths, northern Britain and Eire; early summer.

4 CRANBERRY, *Oxycoccus palustris*. Tiny much-branched shrublet with slender wiry creeping branches; leaves alternate, ovate, shining above, paler and glaucous below, margins recurved; flowers 1–4 at the ends of the branches, on slender hairy stalks; sepals broader than long on top of the inferior ovary; corolla deeply divided into 4 reflexed lobes, pink; stamens 8, anthers with 2 long terminal tails with holes at top; in bogs and marshes on moors, rare in the south.

1 LADY'S BEDSTRAW, *Galium verum*. Perennial herb up to 15 in. 42 from a woody rootstock, covered with minute reflexed hairs; leaves 1-nerved, in whorls of 6 to 8 (half of each whorl are really stipules, as in the following species); flowers yellow, in clusters forming a narrow panicle; fruits slightly 2-lobed, quite smooth; grows in clumps on banks, dunes and in pastures; whole summer.

2 NORTHERN BEDSTRAW, *Galium boreale*. Slender much-branched perennial with smooth or slightly scabrid 4-angled stems; leaves 4 in a whorl, lanceolate to narrowly elliptic, 3-nerved, rough on the margins and midrib below; flowers white, in a terminal leafy panicle; corolla-lobes 4, pointed; fruits olive-brown, densely covered with hooked bristles; north Britain, on rocky slopes and dunes.

3 GREAT HEDGE BEDSTRAW, *Galium mollugo*; perennial herb with stems up to about 4 ft, erect or trailing, with no prickle-like hairs; leaves 1-nerved, usually 8 in a whorl, minutely bristly only on the margin; flowers white, numerous in leafy cymes; corolla-lobes with a fine point; fruits small, smooth or nearly so; in hedges and woods; all summer.

4 HEATH BEDSTRAW, *Galium saxatile*. Slender much-branched perennial with smooth stems and distant whorls of oblanceolate-spathulate leaves, these slightly 'prickly' on the margins, 1-nerved; flowers white, very small in ascending cymes arranged in a leafy lax panicle; corolla-lobes 4, not pointed; fruits bilobed, covered with small tubercles; on barren heaths and commons in acid soils; summer.

5 MARSH BEDSTRAW, *Galium palustre*. Perennial herb with weak stems slightly rough on the angles; leaves 1-nerved, often 6 in a whorl, very blunt, margins slightly rough; flowers white, in lax leafy straggly panicles; corolla-lobes not pointed; fruits deeply divided into 2 rounded almost smooth lobes; in marshy and wet places, sometimes quite in the water; summer.

6 CLEAVERS, GOOSEGRASS, *Galium aparine*. A slender scrambling annual several feet long, clinging to bushes and hedges by means of short recurved hook-like hairs on the quadrangular stems, margins and midrib of the leaves; leaves 6–8 in a whorl, sharply pointed; flowers white, very small, in small leafy axillary clusters; fruits divided into 2 rounded lobes, each densely covered with hooks.

43 1 FEN BEDSTRAW, *Galium uliginosum*. Perennial; stems very weak and straggly, very slightly rough with minute recurved hooks; leaves 6–8 in a whorl, very acute, slightly 'prickly' on the margin and midrib below; flowers very small, white, in little terminal clusters; fruits deeply bilobed, very slightly warted, their stalks deflexed in fruit; in ditches and wet places; summer.

2 WOODRUFF, *Asperula odorata*. Perennial amongst dead leaves under shade of trees; stem smooth; leaves usually 6–8 in a whorl, about $1\frac{1}{2}$ in. long, short stiff hairs on the margin; flowers white, in terminal loose cymes; corolla 4-lobed; stamens 4; fruit globular, covered with fine hooked bristles; whole plant with sweet hay-like scent; spring and early summer.

3 CROSSWORT, *Galium cruciata*. Perennial up to 2 ft long, trailing; rootstock creeping; stems 4-angled, loosely covered with long bristly white hairs; leaves in whorls of 4, two being real leaves and two leafy stipules exactly similar, elliptic-lanceolate, bristly hairy on both surfaces; flowers few in 3-forked axillary clusters, outer flowers bisexual, inner male, yellow; corolla-lobes 4; stamens 4; fruit smooth, deflexed; woods and hedges; spring and early summer.

4 FIELD MADDER, *Sherardia arvensis*. All summer; small annual in cornfields much branched, clothed with stiff short hairs; leaves usually 6 in a whorl, sessile, bristly; flowers violet or pink, in a cluster at the ends of the shoots and surrounded by an involucre of upper leaves; corolla 4-lobed; stamens 4, exserted; fruit crowned by the leafy calyx-lobes.

5 PERIWINKLE, *Vinca minor*. Perennial with slender trailing shoots rooting at lower nodes; leaves opposite, ovate–elliptic, smooth and shining; flowers about 1 to each shoot, axillary, stalked, blue; corolla tubular, with 5 spreading lobes twisted to the left in bud; stamens inserted in the corolla-tube; anthers with hairy tips; fruit of 2 spreading parts; shady places in woods; spring and summer.

1 ASH, *Fraxinus excelsior*. A tall handsome hard-wooded tree; **44** branches opposite; leaves opposite, pinnate, with 3–5 pairs of opposite leaflets with an odd terminal leaflet; flowers appearing in spring before the leaves, arranged in opposite clusters surrounded by a few woody scales; no sepals or petals, but only 2 stamens and an ovary; fruit produced into a wing; a valuable timber.

2 PRIVET, *Ligustrum vulgare*. Known principally for its use as a hedge, often common on chalk downs; leaves opposite, undivided, lanceolate to oblong-elliptic, entire; no stipules; flowers scented, in pyramidal panicles; corolla white, shortly tubular with usually 4 lobes; stamens mostly only 2, exserted; fruit a purple-black globose berry about $\frac{1}{8}$ in. diam.

1 ELDER, *Sambucus nigra*. Small spreading tree with rough bark and **45** wood full of pith; leaves deciduous, opposite, pinnate with 2 or 3 pairs of leaflets and an odd terminal leaflet; flowers in a flat corymb, scented; no bracts; petals yellowish white, united at the base; stamens 5; fruits purple-black and juicy, made into wine and jam or jelly; early summer in woods, hedges and waste places.

2 RED ELDER, *Sambucus racemosa*. Shrub up to 12 ft introduced from gardens, more common in Scotland; April–May; leaflets 5–7, nearly sessile, ovate to elliptic, acuminate, sharply serrate; flowers yellowish white, in a dense ovoid panicle, lower branches usually reflexed; fruit globose, scarlet.

3 GUELDER ROSE, *Viburnum opulus*. Shrub or small tree with attractive *Hydrangea*-like flowers, scented like Hawthorn, in a terminal umbel-like cluster (cyme); outer flowers sterile and white;

leaves opposite, usually 3-lobed and toothed; stalks with a pair of glands at the top; corolla short, 5-lobed; stamens 5; berries blackish red; early summer.

46 1 TWIN-FLOWER, *Linnaea borealis.* Commemorates the name of the 'Father of Modern Botany', *Carl Linnaeus*, of Sweden; a dainty little evergreen shrublet; leaves opposite, rounded-ovate, about ½ in. long and broad; flowers in pairs on a long common stalk; corolla tubular, pale pink or white, 5 lobed; stamens 4, inserted near the base of the corolla; fruit a berry with 1 seed; found only in northern Britain.

2 WOODBINE, HONEYSUCKLE, *Lonicera periclymenum.* Summer and autumn; climbing shrub; leaves opposite; flowers in a terminal cluster, opening in the evening and then sweetly scented, at first white inside, red outside, turning yellowish or brown with age, less scented during the day-time; night flying hawk-moths visit the flowers and effect cross-pollination by transferring pollen from one flower to another; berries red, in a cluster.

3 FLY HONEYSUCKLE, *Lonicera xylosteum.* Early summer; shrub; leaves opposite, broadly elliptic, softly hairy on both surfaces; flowers in pairs on a short common stalk in the leaf-axils subtended by 2 narrow bracts; corolla ⅜ in. long, softly pubescent outside, pale yellow; wild only in one or two southern counties of England; berries red like small currants, in pairs.

4 MOSCHATEL, *Adoxa moschatellina.* Small weak pale-green perennial herb growing in moist shady places; basal leaves on long stalks, divided into 3 parts, each part again divided into 3; stem bearing a pair of opposite smaller leaves; flowers in a cluster at the top of the stem, about 5 together, 1 terminal, the others facing in 4 directions like a town-hall clock, greenish; fruits pendulous on the bent stalk.

47 1 LESSER CELANDINE, *Ficaria verna.* One of our first spring flowers; perennial with numerous finger-like tubers at the root; lowest leaves long-stalked, glossy, broadly triangular; flowers star-like, solitary, closing in bad or dull weather; sepals 3; petals 8 or more, bright yellow and very glossy; stamens numerous; carpels numerous, free; fruitlets containing 1 seed; hedge-banks and shady places in woods.

2 GREAT SPEARWORT, *Ranunculus lingua.* Perennial, in marshes

and ditches; leaves all on the thick hollow stems, linear-lanceolate, tip blunt and pore-like; flowers about 2 in. diam., few in a loose panicle; sepals 5; petals cream-yellow, with a nectary at base; stamens numerous; carpels very numerous, hairless.

3 SPEARWORT, *Ranunculus flammula*. A much smaller 'edition' of *R. lingua* (above) but with radical leaves on long stalks, with broad sheaths at the base, elliptic-lanceolate, blunt, slightly dentate with distant teeth, 3–5 ascending parallel nerves, flowers much smaller, and carpels in fruit forming a small globose head; flowers the whole summer in marshes and wet places.

4 BULBOUS BUTTERCUP, *Ranunculus bulbosus*. A very common species in fields, road-sides, etc.; recognized especially by the bulb-like swelling at the base of the stem and the 5 green reflexed sepals; plant more or less hairy all over; flower-stalks grooved at the top; as in most other buttercups, the petals have a shining surface which acts as a looking glass to insects visiting the flower for the nectar in a pit at their base.

1 CREEPING BUTTERCUP, *Ranunculus repens*. Perennial herb with **48** numerous long stilt-like roots, giving off long runners which root at the nodes and produce new plants; basal leaves with broad membranous sheathing stalks covered with long hairs; greatly resembles *R. bulbosus* but the sepals not reflexed and soon falling off, and no swelling at the base of the stem; May–August, in waste ground and by roadsides.

2 MEADOW CROWFOOT, *Ranunculus acris*. Perennial with very short rootstock; basal leaves on long stalks with sheathing hairy base, more or less orbicular in outline, usually 5-lobed nearly to the base, the lobes again deeply divided; flowers on long stalks forming a lax panicle; stalks not grooved and sepals spreading in the open flower (not reflexed), yellowish green, covered with long hairs; carpels hairless.

3 GOLDILOCKS, *Ranunculus auricomus*. Perennial; basal leaves very variable, from kidney-shaped and coarsely toothed to deeply lobed; stem-leaves cut nearly to the base into 5 narrow parts; sepals 5 or 4; petals 5, or sometimes fewer or absent, then the sepals more yellow; carpels beaked, shortly hairy; in woods and amongst bushes, often in shade.

4 CELERY-LEAVED BUTTERCUP, *Ranunculus sceleratus*. Annual up to 2 ft or more, in wet places and ditches, resembling celery;

stems thick, hollow, ribbed; lower leaves variously 3-lobed to the middle or to the base; sepals 5, soon reflexed and falling off, yellowish-green; petals with a circular pit-like nectary near the base; stamens about 20; carpels very numerous on a conical axis which elongates in fruit; summer.

49 1 HUNGERWEED, CORN BUTTERCUP, *Ranunculus arvensis*. Erect annual herb up to 1½ ft high; basal leaves deeply pinnately lobed, lobes broader than those of the stem-leaves; flowers small, the lowermost well developed into fruit before the others have faded; petals pale yellow; stamens rather few; carpels compressed in fruit and covered with sharp-pointed warts and with bristly margins; common corn-field weed, flowering with the corn; often grows in stackyards.

2 WATER BUTTERCUP, *Ranunculus aquatilis*. Divided into several species, difficult to determine, by some botanists regarded as a very variable species; stems floating in water or creeping in mud; flowers white; carpels small and ovoid, marked with transverse wrinkles; submerged leaves divided into numerous very fine segments, those floating on the surface with broader segments; petals without a scale at the base; late spring and summer.

3 MOUSETAIL, *Myosurus minimus*. A small and inconspicuous annual with a short bare tap root; leaves all basal, linear, up to 3 in. long, 1-nerved; flower-stalks as long as leaves, becoming hollow in the upper part; sepals 5, spurred at base; petals 5, greenish-yellow, with tubular claw and spreading limb; stamens few; carpels very numerous on a long slender axis up to 2 in. long; moist sandy or gravelly places; spring.

4 THREE-LOBED HEPATICA, *Hepatica triloba*. Perennial clothed at the base with long silky hairs; leaves all radical, long-stalked, 3-lobed to about the middle, deeply cordate at the base, lobes broadly ovate, fringed with hairs; flowers solitary, long-stalked; sepals 6–7, bright blue; no petals; stamens numerous; carpels free, beaked in fruit and clothed with long soft hairs; naturalized in shady places from gardens; April, May.

50 1 WOOD ANEMONE, *Anemone nemorosa*. Perennial with black rootstock, in woods in early spring; leaves divided to the base into 3 parts, each part deeply lobed and coarsely toothed; flowering stem bearing a single flower and a whorl of leaves; sepals usually 6, petal-like and white or mauve-pink to purple-blue; no petals; carpels beaked, hairy.

2 YELLOW WOOD ANEMONE, *Anemone ranunculoides*. Very like the above but sepals usually 5 and bright yellow like those of a buttercup; leaves very deeply 3-lobed, the lobes pinnately lobed or coarsely toothed; naturalized from gardens in a few localities in England; April.

3 PASQUE FLOWER, *Anemone pulsatilla*. Perennial herb with thick rootstock; leaves in a bunch on the rootstock, deeply divided to the third degree into narrow acute segments, finely pilose, with long hairs; flowers appearing with the leaves, at first inverted, then spreading or erect, each with a deeply divided leafy bract covered with long silky hairs; sepals mostly 6, blue-violet, hairy outside; no petals; in chalky pastures; spring.

4 PHEASANT'S EYE, *Adonis annua*. Erect annual herb up to 1½ ft high; lower leaves stalked, upper sessile, all deeply 2–3 times pinnate into narrow sharply pointed parts, hairless; flowers solitary; sepals purplish, some 3-toothed; petals a beautiful deep red with a purple mark at the base; stamens 10–15; carpels numerous, in fruit loose on the elongated axis; summer and early autumn.

5 IVY-LEAVED CROWFOOT, *Ranunculus hederaceus*. Herb in muddy places or floating in water; stems rooting at the nodes; leaves opposite or alternate, long-stalked, kidney-shaped, slightly lobed, fleshy, green, hairless, with a half-moon-shape darker band; stalks expanded at the base into a broad membranous sheath; flowers white; stamens few; carpels transversely reticulate in fruit; late spring.

1 YELLOW MEADOW-RUE, *Thalictrum flavum*. Perennial herb up 51 to 3 ft, in moist meadows and along ditches; stem hollow, grooved; leaves alternate, twice pinnate, leaflets about 2–3 pairs and a terminal one, deeply 3-lobed; flowers in a dense terminal panicle; sepals 5, yellow, free; no petals; stamens several, anthers large, yellow; carpels several, strongly ribbed in fruit; summer.

2 TRAVELLER'S JOY, OLD MAN'S BEARD, *Clematis vitalba*. Slender softly woody climber; leaves opposite, pinnate, leaflets usually 5, ovate or ovate-lanceolate, 3-nerved from the base, entire or coarsely toothed; flowers with hawthorn-like odour, in loose axillary panicles; sepals 4, white or greenish; no petals;

carpels numerous, with long feathery tails in fruit; chalky downs of southern England; summer.

3 ALPINE MEADOW-RUE, *Thalictrum alpinum.* Small perennial herb a few inches high, with slender rhizomes; leaves mostly basal, twice ternate, leaflets rounded, bluntly lobed, dark green above, much paler below; flowers in a simple raceme; sepals 5, pale purple, free; no petals; stamens up to 20, filaments pale violet; anthers yellow; carpels ribbed; in mountains from north Wales northward; June–July.

4 MARSH MARIGOLD, *Caltha palustris.* Perennial often in dense tufts, in marshy places by brooks and streams; leaves rounded, deeply cordate at base, crenate, nerves radiating; flowers like those of a buttercup; sepals 5–6, bright yellow and petal-like; no petals; stamens numerous; carpels several, free; nectar secreted on each side near the base of the carpels; plant injurious to stock.

52 1 GLOBE FLOWER, *Trollius europaeus.* A very lovely species in mountains from Wales northwards, flowering in summer; perennial up to 2 ft; leaves divided deeply into about 5 main parts, hairless; flowers solitary, terminal; sepals crowded into a globose mass, rich cream-yellow; petals very narrow; carpels numerous, beaked on one side, containing about 12 ovules.

2 LARKSPUR, *Delphinium ajacis.* Erect annual herb up to 2½ ft; leaves deeply divided into long narrow parts, softly hairy; flowers blue and white or reddish, in a terminal raceme or panicle with leaf-like bracts; sepals 5, terminating below in a single long curved hollow spur; petals 2, united into one and with a spur within the calyx; fruit a follicle with transversely plaited seeds.

3 COLUMBINE, *Aquilegia vulgaris.* Perennial herb up to 2 ft high; basal leaves on long stalks, stalk strongly nerved on the sheathing base, divided into 3 separate leaflets, the leaflets again deeply lobed, glaucous-green and softly hairy below; flowers few in a terminal panicle; sepals 5, coloured; petals 5, blue or dull purple, spurred at the base; woodlands, rare, summer.

4 HERB CHRISTOPHER, BANEBERRY, *Actaea spicata.* Perennial herb up to 2 ft, with leaves like some of the Hemlock family (*Umbelliferae*), triternate, leaflets coarsely and sharply toothed; flowers white, tipped with violet, in a terminal raceme; sepals 4–6, free; petals 4–6, spoon-shaped, clawed; stamens about 15, very conspicuous in flower.

1 WHITE WATER-LILY, *Nymphaea alba*. Aquatic perennial; leaf- **53**
stalks rounded; leaf-blades floating on top of the water, rounded,
deeply cordate, nerves radiating; flowers on long stalks, lying on
the surface of the water, white, not scented, 3–4 in. diam.; sepals
greenish white; petals numerous, gradually changed to stamens;
carpels about 20, united into an ovary; fruit a pulpy berry; June
to September.

2 BRANDY BOTTLE, YELLOW WATER-LILY, *Nuphar lutea*.
Leaves rather like those of the White Water-Lily (above) but more
ovate and with many slender nerves spreading from the midrib;
leaf-stalk flat on the upper surface; flowers elevated above the
water, broadly cup-shaped; sepals 5, green and yellow outside,
yellow inside; petals 12–15, small, broadly wedge-shaped;
stamens in about 6 rows; fruit shaped like a brandy-bottle.

3 GREATER CELANDINE, *Chelidonium majus*. Perennial full of
yellow juice which turns reddish; leaves irregularly pinnate;
flowers in a loose umbel on a long common stalk opposite the leaf;
calyx very small; petals 4, yellow, soon falling; stamens several;
fruit cylindric, up to 2 in. long; seeds with a large crest on one side;
juice reputed to cure warts, applied externally.

4 FUMITORY, *Fumaria officinalis*. Annual, hairless all over, pale
green, often forming a dense spreading tuft up to a foot or two in
diam.; leaves bipinnate, segments often coarsely toothed or lobed;
flowers in slender racemes opposite the leaves, or terminal, the
lower flowers fruiting early; sepals 2, white or coloured; petals 4,
dull purple with darker tips; fruits nearly globose, 1-seeded;
cornfields, waste places and cultivated ground; June, July.

1 FIELD POPPY, *Papaver rhoeas*. Annual up to 2 ft, often very **54**
numerous in cornfields and by roadsides, flowering all summer;
poisonous to stock in green condition; leaves deeply pinnately
divided; flowers solitary on long stalks; sepals 2, soon falling;
petals 4, overlapping and crumpled in bud, rich scarlet, often with
a large black 'eye' at the base, stamens numerous; capsule globose,
with pores near the top.

2 LONG-HEADED POPPY, *Papaver dubium*. Annual with a narrow
carrot-like root, rather similar to the Field Poppy (above) but
leaves narrow and with more side-lobes; flowers salmon-red;
ovary and fruit longer than that of the Field Poppy, tapered to the
base; seeds deeply pitted; also poisonous to stock.

3 PALE POPPY, *Papaver argemone*. Annual; leaves twice deeply divided into narrow lobes, with long weak hairs; sepals 2, bristly outside, soon falling; petals 4, pale red, often with a dark blotch at the base; filaments of stamens swollen; ovary bristly hairy; fruit narrowly oblong, bristly; seeds reticulate.

4 HOLLOW CORYDALIS, *Corydalis cava*. A rare garden escape, in woods; rootstock a hollow tuber; stem without scales at the base, bearing a pair of twice pinnate stalked leaves towards the top, with a terminal raceme of bright red flowers, the latter 2-lipped and with a long spur at the base; capsule beaked by the persistent style and peltate stigma, splitting lengthwise; seeds rounded, black and brightly shining; May.

5 BARBERRY, *Berberis vulgaris*. Spiny shrub; leaves bunched on short shoots; narrowly obovate, very veiny, with sharp fine teeth; flowers yellow, in pendulous racemes; sepals and petals scarcely different; stamens 6, moving into the middle when touched by an insect; anthers opening by flaps; fruit orange red; early summer.

55 1 BLADDER CAMPION, *Silene cucubalus*. Perennial herb branched from the base; leaves opposite, the lowermost withering before flowering, sessile, lanceolate, acute, margins minutely jagged; flowers few, in a loose terminal cluster, some male, some female, some with both sexes; calyx inflated and bladder-like; petals 5, white, deeply 2-lobed; stamens usually 10; styles 3, very slender; capsule opening by 6 teeth; seeds densely warted; summer.

2 NODDING SILENE, NOTTINGHAM CATCHFLY, *Silene nutans*. Perennial herb with a thick taproot, short procumbent barren shoots and erect flowering stems; leaves oblanceolate, narrowed into a long stalk, stem-leaves small, sessile; flowers nodding in a loose panicle, white; calyx tubular, not inflated; petals deeply 2-lobed; styles 3, with the 10 stamens well exserted; capsule opening by 6 teeth; seeds warted; hilly and stony places; summer.

3 SPANISH CATCHFLY, *Silene otites*. Perennial, stems erect up to 1½ ft, sticky; basal leaves narrowly spoon-shaped; stem-leaves few, opposite; flowers of one sex, males on one plant with conspicuous stamens, females on another with conspicuous styles, forming a loose narrow panicle; petals very narrow, green, with coiled tips; stamens 10; styles 3, hairy; only in a few eastern counties; July.

4 MOSS CAMPION, *Silene acaulis*. Perennial mountain herb, forming low dense moss-like clumps; branches very short, crowned by

a rosette of spreading narrow leaves fringed with short teeth; flowers numerous, but single on each branch; calyx tubular, 5-lobed; petals 5, reddish-purple; stamens 10; capsule opening at the top by 6 short teeth; seeds ridged; in northern mountains; summer.

5 RAGGED ROBIN, *Lychnis flos-cuculi*. Perennial with erect weak stems and long internodes; leaves opposite, narrow, fringed with hairs towards the base; flowers in loose terminal clusters; calyx shortly 5-lobed; petals 5, red, deeply cut into 4 linear lobes, the narrow claw with 2 appendages near the middle; stamens 10; capsule ellipsoid, opening by 5 teeth; seeds kidney-shaped, closely warted; spring and summer.

1 WHITE CAMPION, *Lychnis alba*. Strong-growing perennial to 56 3 ft; stem hollow; leaves opposite, oblanceolate, hairy on the nerves; flowers white, of one sex, males on one, females on another plant, opening in the evening and then sweetly scented; calyx 10-ribbed, 5-lobed; petals 5, with a long claw, 2-lobed; styles 5; fruit ovoid, opening by 10 teeth; seeds closely warted; summer.

2 RED CAMPION, *Lychnis dioica*. Biennial up to 2 ft; stems covered with long spreading and shorter reflexed hairs, not sticky; leaves opposite, ovate, more or less 3-nerved from the base; flowers deep pink, of one sex, males on one, females on another plant; calyx 10-ribbed, 5 less prominent, 5-lobed; petals 5, deeply 2-lobed; styles 5; fruit enclosed in the bladder-like expanded calyx, 10-toothed; seeds closely warted; spring and summer.

3 VISCID LYCHNIS, *Lychnis viscaria*. Perennial, tufted; stems up to 1 ft, sticky in the upper part; leaves opposite, long and narrow, lowermost long-stalked, stalks fringed with woolly hairs; flowers red, crowded; calyx tubular, not swollen, 10-nerved, teeth 5; petals slightly notched; north Wales and Scotland, rare; June.

4 ALPINE LYCHNIS, *Lychnis alpina*. Perennial herb with a dense rosette of short linear or narrowly spoon-shaped leaves 1-1½ in. long; flowering stems 6-9 in., bearing 2-4 pairs of narrow leaves; flowers several in a terminal cluster; petals 5, pink, deeply bifid; stamens 10; ovary stipitate; styles 5, free; capsule 5-lobed, lobes recurved; seeds closely warted; mountains of northern Britain, very rare; summer.

1 CORN COCKLE, *Lychnis githago*. Tall coarse annual clothed with 57 long silky hairs; leaves opposite, linear, sessile; flowers scentless,

solitary on long stalks thickened towards the top; calyx-lobes 5, longer than the 5 red notched petals; stamens 10; anthers arrow-shaped; styles 5, free to base; capsule opening by 5 teeth surrounded by enlarged calyx; seeds obovoid, closely warted; poisonous; July, August.

2 MAIDEN PINK, *Dianthus deltoides.* Low-growing perennial up to 1 ft; leaves opposite, linear, 3-nerved, the 2 side nerves near margin; flowers often paired, not scented; calyx deeply 5-lobed, closely nerved; petals pink or white or spotted with white, margin jagged; stamens 10; ovary stipitate; capsule opening by 4 valves; whole summer, on banks and open pastures.

3 PROLIFEROUS PINK, *Dianthus prolifer.* Stiff erect wiry annual with slender forked roots up to 1½ ft high; leaves few, opposite, linear; flowers opening in succession, clustered at the top surrounded by dry broad brown bracts; petals pink to purplish red, very narrow; stamens 10, opening 5 at a time; styles 2; capsule cylindric, 4-valved; southern counties often near the sea; summer and autumn.

4 DEPTFORD PINK, *Dianthus armeria.* Annual or biennial herb up to 2 ft; lower leaves linear-oblanceolate, 1½–2 in. long; stem-leaves narrow, keeled, ascending, shortly hairy; flowers in terminal clusters surrounded by leafy bracts equally as long; bracteoles 2, ribbed, as long as the calyx, the latter tubular with 5 short acute teeth; petals 5, deep red with pale dots, claw white; capsule as long as calyx; rare and local, in hedgerows and dry pastures; July, August.

58 1 WOOD STARWORT, *Stellaria nemorum.* Perennial with creeping rootstock; stems with short spreading hairs; leaves ovate, pointed, lower on long stalks, upper becoming sessile; flowers in dainty loose spreading cymes on long slender stalks, white; petals very deeply 2-lobed, lobes narrow; styles 3; capsule opening nearly to the base into 6 valves; seeds warted; summer.

2 CHICKWEED, *Stellaria media.* A weed well known to every gardener; annual, with a line of reflexed hairs along one side of the branches; leaves opposite, ovate, stalks hairy; flowers scarcely stalked but on long stalks in fruit; 5 petals shorter than the 5 sepals and deeply 2-lobed, white; stamens 5 or 3 or 2; anthers pink when young; styles 3; capsule opening by 6 short teeth; seeds curved, warted.

3 GREATER STITCHWORT, GREAT STARWORT, *Stellaria holostea*.
Perennial with weak stems in hedges and amongst bushes; stems
quadrangular, hairless; leaves opposite, narrow, sharply pointed,
minute comb-like teeth on the margin; flowers showy, in leafy
panicles; sepals 5, acute; petals 5, white, divided nearly to the
middle; stamens 10; styles 3, free; capsule opening by 3 valves;
seeds kidney-shaped, warted; spring to early summer.

4 HEATH STITCHWORT, *Stellaria graminea*. Perennial; stems
sharply 4-angled, not hairy; leaves opposite, narrow, acute;
flowers many but very laxly arranged; stalks up to 1½ in. long;
sepals 5, outermost without hairs, the others with short hairs on the
margin; petals 5 but appearing like 10, being deeply divided
almost to the base, white; stamens 10; styles 3; seeds orbicular,
verrucose; dry pastures, hedgebanks, May to August.

5 FIELD CHICKWEED, *Cerastium arvense*. Perennial herb; branches
covered all around with deflexed hairs; leaves opposite, linear,
entire, hairy all over; flowers 3–5 together, white; petals 5, twice
as long as the 5 sepals, deeply 2-lobed; stamens usually 10; styles 5,
free; capsule oblique, opening at the top by 10 teeth; seeds rounded,
warted all over; sandy fields and waste ground; spring to early
summer.

1 ALPINE MOUSE-EAR CHICKWEED, *Cerastium alpinum*. Peren- 59
nial herb with prostrate woody stems and ascending shoots, often
forming mats; stems and leaves densely covered with soft white
hairs and a few glands; leaves opposite, ovate or elliptic; bracts
with narrow membranous margins; flowers 1–4 at the ends of the
shoots, ¾ in. diam.; sepals with narrow thin margins and often
violet tips; petals white, twice as long as calyx; northern Britain;
June–August.

2 COMMON MOUSE-EAR CHICKWEED, *Cerastium vulgatum*.
Small annual herb, hairy and glandular; stem-leaves ovate to
elliptic, sessile, clothed with short white hairs; flowers very small,
in terminal cymes; stalks glandular; sepals glandular-hairy; petals
white, shorter than the sepals, slightly notched; stamens 5; styles 5;
capsule a little longer than the sepals, opening by 10 teeth; seeds
tubercled; dry open places; April, May.

3 LITTLE MOUSE-EAR CHICKWEED, *Cerastium semidecandrum*.
Small annual herb with erect or ascending stems, hairy with
some of the hairs glandular; stem-leaves ovate to oblong, sessile,

shortly hairy; flowers in short cymes, oldest flower in the middle, stalks glandular; calyx deeply 5-lobed, lobes with broad white margins; petals white, shorter than sepals; stamens 5; styles 5; capsule 10-toothed; seeds tuberculate; dry open or sandy soils; spring.

4 THYME-LEAVED SANDWORT, *Arenaria serpyllifolia*. A very tiny annual a few inches long, covered with minute reflexed scabrid hairs; leaves opposite, very small, ovate, 3–5-nerved from the base; flowers in the upper leaf-axils, white; petals 5, smaller than the sepals; stamens 10; styles 3, twisted; capsule ovoid, opening by 6 short teeth; seeds kidney-shaped, warted in transverse rows; on dry walls and sandy waste places; summer.

5 THREE-NERVED SANDWORT, *Arenaria trinervia*. Delicate decumbent or spreading annual up to 1 ft long; stem and branches with recurved hairs mainly on one side; leaves opposite, ovate or ovate-elliptic, narrowed to the winged short stalks, with 3 distinct parallel nerves from base to apex; flowers usually only 1 from the axil of each pair of leaves, white; petals shorter than sepals; stamens 10; styles 3; capsule 6-valved; seeds brown, grooved.

6 SEA PURSLANE, *Arenaria peploides*. Perennial with creeping rootstock; stems much branched like the leaves rather fleshy; leaves opposite, in 4 rows, sessile, ovate-elliptic, green, with thin and slightly frilled margins; flowers solitary in the forks and upper leaf-axils; sepals 5, green and fleshy; petals 5, white, very tiny; stamens 10; styles 3–5; capsule opening by 3–5 valves; maritime in sand or shingle; used for pickling.

60 1 KNOTTED PEARLWORT, *Sagina nodosa*. Small tufted perennial, often flowering the first year; leaves bunched at the base, opposite, needle-like, acute, upper leaves smaller; no stipules; flowers few, on slender stalks; sepals 5, shorter than the 5 narrowly obovate white petals; stamens 10; styles 5; fruit splitting into 5 parts; seeds very minute.

2 PROCUMBENT PEARLWORT, *Sagina procumbens*. A tiny tufted perennial, flowering from the seedling stage; stems spreading; leaves in a dense rosette, linear or needle-like, sharply pointed; stem-leaves opposite; no stipules; flowers few, axillary and solitary and terminal; sepals 4, sometimes tinged with crimson; petals 4, very small, or absent; stamens 4; styles 4, short and hairy; fruit splitting into 4 parts; seeds warted; spring to autumn.

3 SPURRY, *Spergula arvensis*. Slender annual weed; leaves in clusters at the nodes and appearing to be whorled, almost needle-like, up to about 1 in. long; stipules present, very small and dry; flowers numerous in terminal forked cymes, the slender stalks turning down as the flowers mature; sepals 5; petals 5.

4 SAND SPURRY, *Spergularia rubra*. Annual or biennial herb in open sandy or gravelly places; branches decumbent, slender, glandular in the upper parts; leaves linear, tip awned, up to ¾ in. long; stipules lanceolate, split at the tip, silvery and conspicuous; flowers rather few at the ends of the shoots, rosy-red; sepals and petals 5.

5 RUPTURE WORT, *Herniaria glabra*. Herb with numerous pros-trate radiating branches; lower leaves opposite, upper alternate, oblanceolate to elliptic, very small, at most ⅓ in. long; stipules scarious, broad; flowers very small, clustered in the leaf-axils; calyx green, deeply 5-lobed; petals absent; stamens 5, alternate with as many staminodes; stigmas 2; fruit enclosed by the calyx, 1-seeded; seed black-brown.

6 ANNUAL KNAWEL, *Scleranthus annuus*. Much-branched annual herb; leaves opposite, linear, about 1 in. long, united at the base; flowers very small, numerous and crowded in small terminal cymes, sessile in the forks; calyx tubular, 5-lobed; petals absent; stamens 5, alternating with short staminodes; ovary free from the calyx, 1-locular, with one ovule pendulous from a basal thread; weed in fields and waste places; all summer.

1 GOOSEFOOT, FAT HEN, *Chenopodium album*. Annual herb up **61** to 2 ft, pale green or mealy white; leaves alternate, stalked, lower more or less triangular or almost rhomboid, bluntly toothed, often completely covered by rounded whitish papillae; flowers bisexual, in short dense axillary spikes; calyx 5-lobed; no petals; stamens 5; styles mostly 3; weed on rubbish-heaps; formerly used as a potherb, boiled and eaten like spinach.

2 HASTATE ORACHE, *Atriplex hastata*. Annual; lower leaves opposite, triangular, with spreading basal lobes, more or less toothed, smooth or mealy only below; flowers in branched slightly leafy spikes collected into a panicle; bracteoles united only at the very base; August, September; in waste places, mostly near the sea.

3 COMMON ORACHE, *Atriplex patula*. Erect annual rather like Goosefoot (above) but lower leaves mostly opposite, triangular

with 2 spreading lobes (hastate) at base, smooth or minutely mealy-papillous; flowers of one sex, male and female on the same plant, in slender spikes, mostly covered with mealy papillae; sepals 5; no petals; stamens 5; female flowers with 2 herbaceous toothed bracts which enlarge in fruit, latter black and hard.

4 SHORE ORACHE, *Atriplex littoralis*. By some botanists regarded as a form of *A. patula* (above), but stems prostrate, often striped with green or red, the branches ascending and lower leaves very narrow, entire or toothed, mostly alternate; flowers as in *A. patula*.

5 MARSH GLASSWORT or SAMPHIRE, *Salicornia herbacea*. Fleshy annual or biennial herb with jointed stems without proper leaves, often in great quantity in salt marshes; flower-spike terminal, $\frac{1}{2}$–1 in. long; flowers immersed in the upper joints, 3 in a triangle on each side; calyx succulent, flat and nearly closed at the top, the 2 or 1 stamens exserted from the minutely toothed mouth; no petals; stigmas 2–3; summer and autumn.

62 1 MARSH GENTIAN, *Gentiana pneumonanthe*. Summer; perennial herb up to 2 ft; leaves opposite, sessile, lanceolate to linear, the broader with 3 parallel nerves; lower flowers often paired, axillary; calyx with 2 leafy bracts at the base, 5-lobed; corolla $1\frac{1}{2}$ in. long, tinged with green outside, the lobes a beautiful deep blue; stamens 5; moist places on heaths; a favourite garden plant.

2 SMALL ALPINE GENTIAN, *Gentiana nivalis*. Rare little alpine plant found only in Scotland; stems a few inches high, mostly unbranched; radical leaves obovate; stem-leaves elliptic, shortly connate at the base; flowers solitary, terminal and axillary; calyx-tube cylindric, indistinctly 5-angled; lobes 5, shorter than the tube; corolla deep vivid blue, tube without hairs in the throat; July–September.

3 FIELD GENTIAN, *Gentiana campestris*. Late summer and autumn; erect annual up to 9 in.; leaves opposite, increasing in size upwards, broadly lanceolate, 3-nerved; flowers axillary; calyx leaf-like, 4-lobed to about the middle, outer lobes much broader than inner; corolla pale blue, 4-lobed, fringed with long blue hairs at the mouth; stamens 4, pastures and commons mostly in limestone soil.

4 CENTAURY, *Centaurium minus*. A very distinct little annual in dry pastures and sandy banks, flowering all summer; basal leaves forming a rosette, prominently 3-nerved from the base; stem-

leaves small, sessile; flowers deep pink, in a dense repeatedly forked cyme; calyx deeply lobed into 5 parts; corolla 5-lobed, lobes twisted in bud; anthers 5, spirally coiled after opening.

5 BUCKBEAN, *Menyanthes trifoliata*. Early summer; aquatic herb with a dense mat of roots; leaves alternate, divided into 3 separate obovate leaflets; flowers several in a loose raceme on a long stalk arising from below the tuft of leaves; calyx deeply 5-lobed; corolla 5-lobed, lobes not overlapping in bud, densely hairy inside; some flowers have long styles, some short styles.

1 BUTTERWORT, *Pinguicula vulgaris*. Herb in mountain bogs or on **63** wet rocks; leaves in a rosette, ovate to oblong, fleshy and covered with small crystalline points and clammy to the touch; calyx 5-lobed to the middle; corolla bluish-purple, 2-lipped, upper lip shorter than lower, latter 3-lobed, tube spurred at base; stamens 2; early summer.

2 BLADDERWORT, *Utricularia vulgaris*. Aquatic floating herb like a fine green seaweed, with long root-like capillary branches, all submerged; leaves much divided into toothed segments bearing here and there small green bladders full of air which trap small animals; flowers yellow, above the water; sepals 2; corolla 2-lipped and spurred; stamens 2; summer.

3 COWSLIP, *Primula veris*. Perennial with a dense tuft of finely toothed leaves; common flower-stalks several from the tuft, bearing at the top an umbel of several stalked scented flowers with a whorl of narrow bracts; corolla cream-yellow, with an orange 'eye'; style either long or short; stamens inserted either in the middle or near the top of the tube; spring.

4 MEALY or BIRD'S-EYE PRIMROSE, *Primula farinosa*. Found only in northern Britain, in mountain pastures; perennial with leaves in a rosette, toothed, green above, densely covered below with a whitish or greenish-white meal; common flower-stalk mealy towards the top; flowers umbellate, lovely pale lilac with a yellow 'eye'; style and stamens as in *P. veris*; spring.

5 NORTHERN ANDROSACE, *Androsace septentrionalis*. A cultivated plant sometimes found outside gardens or rockeries; annual; leaves in a rosette, narrowly spathulate, toothed, pointed, ciliate; umbels several- to many-flowered; flowers very small, white; corolla-lobes 5, slightly longer than the 5 sepals, with as many stamens inserted opposite to them.

64 1 WATER VIOLET, *Hottonia palustris*. Aquatic perennial herb with a long trailing rhizome, with vertical aerial branches; leaves in a basal rosette, pinnate into many narrow lobes; above the leaves a whorl of branches; flowers numerous in whorls on an upright axis; corolla lilac with a yellow 'eye'; stamens 5, opposite the lobes; styles and stamens short or long; early summer in ponds and marshes.

2 TRIENTALE, *Trientalis europaea*. Perennial herb about 6 in. high; leaves about 6, in a bunch, broadly oblanceolate; flowers one or more from the whorl of leaves; sepals 6–7, narrow; corolla 6–7-lobed, white or pale pink with a yellow ring; stamens opposite the corolla-lobes; in woods, often among pines and birches in northern Britain; June, July.

3 SEA MILKWORT, *Glaux maritima*. On sands, salt-marshes and muddy places near the sea; small perennial, slightly fleshy; rootstock creeping, rooting at the nodes; lower leaves opposite, upper alternate, entire; no stipules; flowers axillary, forming a leafy spike-like raceme; sepals 5, pale pink and resembling petals, the latter absent; stamens 5, alternating with the sepals.

4 SCARLET PIMPERNEL, POOR MAN'S WEATHER-GLASS, *Anagallis arvensis*. Small annual in cornfields, gardens and waste places; leaves opposite, sessile, ovate, 3-nerved from the base; flowers usually red, axillary, solitary; calyx deeply 5-lobed; corolla-tube short, lobes 5, fringed with small glands; stamens 5, opposite the corolla-lobes, stalks (filaments) fringed with several-celled hairs; spring to autumn.

65 1 GREATER PLANTAIN, *Plantago major*. Perennial, glabrous or pubescent; leaves all radical, abruptly contracted at the base, ovate to elliptic, 5–9-nerved lengthwise; spikes on unfurrowed peduncles scarcely longer than the leaves; corolla yellowish-white; anthers at first lilac, at length brownish yellow; in open places, often in farmyards and by roads; May–September; flowers wind-pollinated.

2 HOARY PLANTAIN, *Plantago media*. Perennial herb, finely pubescent; leaves all radical, spreading, obscurely toothed, elliptic to ovate, with 5–9 longitudinal nerves, gradually narrowed at the base; spikes on long unfurrowed peduncles much exceeding the leaves; flowers scented; corolla whitish, tube glabrous; filaments pu·ple; anthers lilac or white; in grassy places; May–August; flowers insect-pollinated.

3 RIBWORT PLANTAIN, *Plantago lanceolata*. A very common perennial plant in meadows and by road-sides; leaves all radical, erect or spreading, lanceolate, minutely and distantly toothed on the margin with 3–6 longitudinal nerves and gradually narrowed into the petiole; spikes ovoid or oblong, about 1 in. long, on long deeply furrowed peduncles much exceeding the leaves; corolla-tube glabrous, lobes with brown midrib; stamens white; April–August; flowers wind-pollinated.

4 SEA PLANTAIN, *Plantago maritima*. Perennial; stem woody; leaves all radical, linear and grass-like but fleshy, very faintly nerved, hairless; spikes on unfurrowed peduncles as long as or longer than the leaves; corolla hairy; anthers pale yellow; in salt marshes by the sea and beside streams on mountains; flowers wind-pollinated; June–August.

5 BUCKSHORN PLANTAIN, *Plantago coronopus*. Common in sea-side areas but also inland; biennial or perennial; leaves very variable, all radical, from narrow and entire to deeply pinnately lobed, 1-nerved, pubescent; spikes on unfurrowed peduncles usually longer than the leaves; bracts with long spreading points; anthers pale yellow; May to July; flowers wind-pollinated.

1 YELLOW LOOSESTRIFE, *Lysimachia vulgaris*. Perennial with **66** erect stems to about 3 ft, on shady banks near water; leaves in whorls or the upper in pairs, lanceolate; flowers in leafy terminal panicles, yellow; sepals 5; corolla with a short broad tube, 5-lobed, lobes twisted in bud, densely glandular above; stamens 5, opposite the lobes; filaments glandular; late summer.

2 CREEPING JENNY, MONEYWORT, *Lysimachia nummularia*. Perennial, stems prostrate, rooting at nodes; leaves opposite, ovate-rounded, entire, bright green; no stipules; flowers axillary; sepals eared at base; corolla of 5 nearly separate petals, rich butter-cup-yellow, about 1 in. diam.; stamens 5, opposite the lobes, filaments shortly hairy; summer and autumn; on banks and under hedges.

3 TUFTED LOOSESTRIFE, *Lysimachia thyrsiflora*. Perennial erect herb up to 2 ft high, in wet places and in shallow water; leaves opposite, rarely whorled, sessile, lanceolate, densely spotted with black glands; flowers in short pedunculate racemes in the axils of the leaves about the middle of the stem; corolla pale yellow, with 5 narrow lobes; stamens 5, opposite the lobes; June–July.

4 SEA THRIFT, *Armeria maritima*. Tufted perennial herb often common by the sea, in muddy and sandy places and on rocks as well as on some inland mountains; easily recognized by the head of pink or sometimes white flowers on a long common stalk, the outer bracts of the involucre longer than the others and elongated at the base forming a reflexed sheath around the top; April to September.

67 1 VIVIPAROUS POLYGONUM, *Polygonum viviparum*. Perennial erect herb up to 1 ft high with a thick tuberous rootstock, on ledges of rocks and in wet places by streams, flowering in June and July; basal leaves on long slender stalks, narrow, with numerous much-branched side-nerves; flowers in a slender solitary spike, often the lower flowers converted into little bulbils with crimson base and green tip; stamens 8; styles 3; fruit smooth.

2 FLOATING POLYGONUM, *Polygonum amphibium*. Perennial with slender woody rootstock in ditches and ponds flowering during summer; when growing away from water stems creeping at base and leaves often hairy; leaves stalked, with a large sheathing stipule at the base, lanceolate, 4–5 in. long, minutely toothed, lateral nerves numerous, repeatedly looped; flowers in a thick spike-like raceme, pink to purple red; stamens 6; style deeply divided into 2 parts.

3 PEACHWORT, RED-SHANKS, *Polygonum persicaria*. Annual with reddish branches; leaves lanceolate, with a thin tubular stipule at the base fringed with slender bristles; flowers red or greenish, in often paired spike-like racemes up to 1½ in. long; stamens 5–6; fruit nearly black, shining; in ditches, by roadsides and on rubbish heaps; summer and autumn.

4 WATERPEPPER, *Polygonum hydropiper*. Slender annual in wet places, stream and pond-sides, and in damp gullies in woods; stems often reddish; leaves narrow, fringed with short hairs, with a tubular fringed stipule within the base; flowers in slender racemes, green and pink, purplish outside; stamens about 6; fruit black, 3-angled, pitted; when chewed leaves taste as hot as pepper.

5 BLACK BINDWEED, *Polygonum convolvulus*. Annual with twining ribbed stem; leaves rounded-ovate, widely sagittate – heart-shaped at base, long-pointed, entire; stipules very short; flowers shortly stalked, in axillary clusters or short racemes, green and white; stamens 5; styles 3; fruit triangular, black and shining; waste places and arable land.

54

6 Knotweed, Knotgrass, *Polygonum aviculare*. Much branched wiry annual and a troublesome weed flowering and fruiting nearly the whole season; usually prostrate, with stems or branches up to 2 ft long when growing amongst crops or long grass; leaves narrow, with adnate stipules at the base which soon split and become jagged on the margin; stamens 8; fruits triangular, beaked, pitted.

1 Sheep Sorrel, *Rumex acetosella*. Acid slender perennial plant **68** often a troublesome weed, known to have caused poisoning in stock; stems reddish or green and red; leaves alternate, narrowly lanceolate, entire except for two spreading lobes near the base; stipules conspicuous, soon splitting; flowers very small, often of one sex, pollinated by the wind; fruit embraced by the inner sepals, outer sepals remaining erect.

2 Sorrel, *Rumex acetosa*. Stems usually unbranched up to 2 ft high, often turning red; lower leaves oblong or broadly lanceolate, arrow-shaped at the base with broad pointed lobes, bright green and very acid; flowers of one sex, either on the same or on different plants, in long terminal leafless panicles, often turning red; inner segments of the fruiting calyx enlarged, orbicular, thin and almost like petals, at length reflexed on the stalk; meadows and moist pastures; summer.

3 Grainless Curled Dock, *Rumex longifolius*. Robust erect perennial up to 4 ft high; basal leaves large, 6–15 in. long, with wavy crenate margins, oblong-elliptic, rather cordate at the base; floral leaves narrow, becoming stalkless; panicle compact; sepals in fruit thin and rounded-kidney-shaped, nearly entire, without tubercles; by rivers and ditches and in damp grassy places; June–July.

4 Curled Dock, *Rumex crispus*. Perennial herb up to 3 ft; basal leaves long and narrow with wavy margins, 6–8 in. long, stalked, the upper leaves gradually smaller and sessile; flowers numerous in panicles of whorls; stalks jointed below the middle; calyx-lobes in fruit broadly ovate, cordate, one lobe with an ovoid or oblong coloured tubercle on the outside; June to August.

5 Kidney Sorrel, *Oxyria digyna*. Perennial herb up to 1 ft; leaves mostly basal, transversely oblong or kidney-shaped, up to 2½ in. broad, thin, hairless, with about 7 nerves spreading from the base; flowers in a terminal panicle subtended by a small leaf; sepals 4;

stamens 6; ovary with 2 much divided stigmas; fruit flat, obovate, broadly winged; only on mountains in northern Britain; summer.

69 1 ROSE BAY, *Chamaenerion angustifolium*. A beautiful plant but troublesome weed; stems reddish, up to 4 ft; leaves numerous, alternate, ascending, narrowly lanceolate to almost linear, about 6 in. long, with numerous looped nerves; flowers in a terminal raceme up to 1 ft long; sepals 4; petals 4, purplish-red; stamens 8; ovary inferior, long and narrow below the calyx; fruit about 2 in.; seeds with a tuft of long slender hairs at the end; in light soil in open woods and bombed sites; summer.

2 GREAT WILLOW HERB, CODLINS-AND-CREAM, *Epilobium hirsutum*. Rank growing herb up to 5 ft, softly hairy all over, by ditches and streams; leaves opposite, lanceolate, toothed; upper leaves alternate; flowers axillary in the upper leaves; buds with 4 slender tips; sepals 4; petals 4, deeply notched; stamens 8, 4 long and 4 shorter; ovary below the calyx, deeply grooved; seeds with a tuft of hairs at one end; summer.

3 MOUNTAIN WILLOW HERB, *Epilobium montanum*. Perennial; stems up to 2 ft; leaves alternate or opposite, narrowly ovate, toothed, minutely hairy; flowers stalked below the long stalk-like inferior ovary; sepals 4; petals 4, pink, deeply 2-lobed; fruits $2-3\frac{1}{2}$ in. long; seeds tipped with a brush of long fine hairs; shady banks, old walls and roofs, often a weed.

4 MARSH WILLOW HERB, *Epilobium palustre*. Perennial with slender softly hairy stems in wet boggy places, flowering in summer; leaves opposite, the upper becoming alternate, lanceolate to almost linear; flowers very few to solitary at the tops of the stems, stalked, rosy-lilac; sepals 4; petals 4, deeply notched; stamens 8; fruit up to 3 in. long; seeds with a tuft of hairs at the end.

5 ALPINE WILLOW HERB, *Epilobium alpinum*. A small perennial herb; leaves opposite, oblanceolate, very slightly toothed, about 1 in. long, not hairy; flowers 1–2 in the upper axils, long-stalked besides the long stalk-like inferior ovary; petals notched; stigma club-shaped, entire; fruits $1\frac{1}{2}-2$ in. long; northern Britain; summer.

6 ENCHANTER'S NIGHTSHADE, *Circaea lutetiana*. Perennial herb with slender creeping rootstock, often in great abundance in woods and shady places, but rare in Scotland; stems up to 2 ft; leaves opposite, stalked, ovate, broadly pointed, toothed, nerves

looped within the margin; flowers in slender terminal and axillary racemes, pendulous; sepals 2, crimson; petals 2, white or pink; fruits covered with slender hooked bristles.

70

1 MARESTAIL, *Hippuris vulgaris*. Rather like Horsetail (*Equisetum*); aquatic perennial in ponds and ditches; stem unbranched, upper part rising above the water for about 1 ft; leaves in whorls of 8–12, linear; flowers very small, sessile, axillary; calyx very reduced; no petals; stamen 1, anther reddish; ovary inferior; fruit a small ellipsoid nut with 1 seed; early June to late summer; flowers wind-pollinated.

2 SEA BUCKTHORN, *Hippophae rhamnoides*. A seaside shrub or small tree rather like a willow, but covered all over with silvery scales; axillary shoots often spine-tipped; leaves alternate, narrow, densely scaly below; flowers of one sex, males on one bush, females on another, males in short catkins; fruits berry-like, brown or yellow.

3 MEZEREON, SPURGE OLIVE, *Daphne mezereum*. A lovely plant now rare in a wild state but in many cottage gardens; flowers in woodlands often as early as January or February, before the leaves; calyx petal-like, pink, tubular, 4-lobed; stamens 8, in 2 rows in the tube; ovary bottle-shaped, with a nearly sessile 2-lobed stigma; leaves lanceolate; fruit a round red berry.

4 PURPLE LOOSESTRIFE, *Lythrum salicaria*. Perennial; stems erect, up to 3 ft, in wet ditches and by ponds and rivers; leaves opposite or 3 in a whorl, sessile, lanceolate, shortly hairy below; flowers in a dense terminal spike-like raceme, with small green bracts throughout; calyx tubular, ribbed, 6–8-lobed; petals often 6, reddish purple or pink with darker veins; stamens twice as many as petals; ovary free within the calyx-tube.

71

1 ROSE-ROOT STONECROP, *Sedum roseum*. Perennial amongst rocks on hills and mountains in northern Britain and Eire; rhizome with a bunch of brown scales at the top; stems scaly towards the base, the scales gradually changed into alternate to subwhorled oblong-lanceolate sessile fleshy leaves dentate towards the apex; flowers in a terminal cluster (corymb), orange-yellow; petals linear; stamens and carpels free, latter curved and beaked in fruit.

2 ORPINE, LIVELONG, *Sedum telephium*. Perennial herb with annual stems, erect, about 1 ft high; leaves scattered or opposite, sessile to

shortly stalked, obovate or oblong, coarsely toothed; flowers pale yellow to purplish, forming a corymb; sepals 5, short, pointed; petals more than twice as long; stamens 10, shorter than the petals; carpels 5, free; in fields, hedge-banks and bushy places; late summer.

3 SPURIOUS STONECROP, *Sedum spurium*. Creeping perennial forming large mats with numerous ascending branches; leaves opposite, flat, obovate, crenate-serrate above the middle, hairy on the margins, shortly stalked; flowers in dense flat terminal cymes; petals pink, rarely white or crimson, suberect; carpels erect; July, August; introduced from cultivation.

4 STONECROP, *Sedum acre*. Grows in tufts on walls and rocks and in sandy places, often on golf courses; stems procumbent, like the leaves very succulent and bitter to taste, sometimes called Wall-pepper; leaves alternate or opposite, ovoid to nearly globose, densely crowded; flowers crowded at the top of the shoots, bright yellow; stamens 10; carpels 5, free, opening on the inner side; summer.

5 WHITE SEDUM, *Sedum album*. Rootstock creeping, bearing in winter short barren stems with crowded leaves, in summer erect flowering branches up to 6 in. high; leaves alternate, $\frac{1}{4}-\frac{1}{2}$ in. long, as thick as broad; flowers white or slightly pink, small and numerous in terminal corymbs; sepals 5, short, obtuse; petals 5, nearly 3 times as long, obtuse; on old walls, rocks, cottage roofs; summer.

72 1 STAR SAXIFRAGE, *Saxifraga stellaris*. Perennial herb on wet rocks and by water, only in northern Britain and Eire; leaves in tufts, oblanceolate, with a few teeth, sprinkled with hairs above; flowering stems up to 5 in., leafy only near the base; flowers white, few on each common stalk; sepals 5, soon reflexed; petals 5, free, spreading, with 2 yellow spots at base; stamens 10; styles 2.

2 ALPINE SAXIFRAGE, *Saxifraga nivalis*. Perennial herb with thick erect rootstock crowned by a tuft of spreading ovate-cuneate coarsely dentate leaves, these thick and leathery, stalk hairy, otherwise hairless, up to 1 in. long; flowers few on a common stalk; petals 5, rounded-obovate; stamens 10, carpels 2, free nearly to the base, tips in fruit recurved like a parrot's beak; only in mountains of northern Britain and Eire.

3 PURPLE SAXIFRAGE, *Saxifraga oppositifolia*. A lovely dwarf alpine species, a favourite for rock gardens; mountains of northern

Britain, common in Scotland; perennial creeping herb, much branched, forming dense carpets; leaves crowded, opposite, margins with bristly hairs, tip thickened; flowers numerous, bluish-purple; stamens 10; carpels 2, free nearly to base; spring and early summer.

4 YELLOW MOUNTAIN SAXIFRAGE, *Saxifraga aizoides*. Perennial; lower leaves becoming reflexed, remainder spreading or ascending, alternate, sessile, narrow, entire or sharply toothed; flowers in a loose raceme-like cyme, the oldest flower at the top; petals yellow, with orange-spots, 3-nerved; stamens 10; capsule semi-inferior, with 2 suberect styles; on wet rocks and near rills and springs in northern Britain; summer and autumn.

5 DROOPING SAXIFRAGE, *Saxifraga cernua*. Perennial herb up to 6 in.; lower leaves long-petiolate, palmately 5–3-lobed, hairless; stem bearing gradually smaller leaves below the 1–3 white nodding flowers, the upper leaves often with little bulbils in their axils; stamens 10; carpels 2, united to the top but with 2 free styles; rare at the top of one or two Scottish mountains.

1 MARSH SAXIFRAGE, *Saxifraga hirculus*. On wet moors in north- **73** ern England, Scotland and Eire; August; perennial with slender spreading leafy stolons; leaves narrow, entire; flowers yellow, 1–2 at the top of the leafy stem, the latter with crispate hairs towards the top; stamens 10; carpels 2, connate, styles divergent.

2 RUE-LEAVED SAXIFRAGE, *Saxifraga tridactylites*. Erect annual covered all over with short gland-tipped hairs; leaves alternate or rarely opposite, deeply 3–5-lobed; calyx-tube united high up with the ovary; petals 5, white, small, obovate, 3-nerved; stamens 10; ovary inferior; on walls and rocks, spring and early summer.

3 MEADOW SAXIFRAGE, *Saxifraga granulata*. Perennial with small globose bulb-like structures at the base; lower leaves kidney-shaped, coarsely toothed, few on the stem, stalks and margins fringed with white hairs; flowers few in terminal cymes, white, the central one opening first and markedly different from the others in having large fat papillous stigmas borne on long styles; calyx-tube covered with gland-tipped hairs; in meadows; spring.

4 ALTERNATE GOLDEN SAXIFRAGE, *Chrysosplenium alternifolium*. A delicate perennial herb crowded in wet shady places and rillsides, flowering in spring; stems a few inches high, rooting at the nodes; leaves alternate, orbicular to obovate, widely cordate,

undulate on the margin, those around the flowers often yellowish; stem divided into 2 at the top; flowers yellow or greenish; calyx 4-lobed; no petals; stamens 8; disk crenate.

5 GRASS OF PARNASSUS, *Parnassia palustris*. Perennial herb; basal leaves long-stalked, rounded or ovate, 5–7-nerved from the cordate base; flowers single on long stalks with a large leaf-like bract about the middle; petals 5, white, free; stamens 5, alternate with petals, alternating with 5 yellow-green staminodes deeply divided into thread-like parts tipped by a glistening gland; ovary superior, 1-locular; in bogs; end of summer.

74 1 PIMPINEL, BURNET SAXIFRAGE, *Pimpinella saxifraga*. Perennial with thick rootstock; stems up to 2 ft, slender and wiry; basal leaves once pinnate, leaflets coarsely toothed, stem-leaves twice pinnately lobed with narrower divisions; umbels usually in pairs, all without bracts; rays 10–18, very slender; flowers white; fruits ovoid-elliptic, scarcely compressed, each half with 5 ribs; all summer, in pastures and by roadsides.

2 CARAWAY, *Carum carvi*. Provides the 'seeds' used in cooking; biennial herb; root carrot-like; stem up to 2 ft; basal leaves long-stalked, twice or thrice pinnate, with narrow 1-nerved divisions; stem-leaves with sheathing base up to $1\frac{1}{2}$ in. long; main umbel with linear bracts, smaller umbels without bracts; flowers white; fruits oblong, with 5 ribs on each half, axis splitting to base when ripe; spring, early summer.

3 GOUTWEED, BISHOP'S WEED, HERB GERRARD, *Aegopodium podagraria*. An aggressive perennial and a noxious weed to farmers and gardeners, flowering from June to August; radical leaves often forming a complete carpet on the soil, twice ternate, leaflets elliptic or ovate, coarsely toothed; umbels of small white flowers often 3 together on each shoot; no bracts; fruits with 5 slender ribs but no resin lines.

4 WOOD SANICLE, *Sanicula europaea*. Perennial; leaves nearly all basal, long-stalked, rounded or pentagonal in outline, divided almost to the base into 5 obovate lobulate toothed lobes; main umbel with a whorl of toothed leafy bracts, smaller head-like umbels with small bracts; flowers of one sex, males in 2 or 3 rows around the females; petals white; fruits covered with hooked prickles; in woods; May, June.

5 SEA HOLLY, *Eryngium maritimum*. Very easily recognized, only

found near the sea, in July and August; leaves alternate, clasping the stem, holly-like and with sharply prickly margins; stem solid, nearly white; flowers lavender-blue, crowded into sessile heads surrounded by a whorl of leaves; fruits ovoid, prickly.

1 WILD PARSNIP, *Pastinaca sativa*. Annual or biennial 2–3 ft on **75** roadsides and waste places; tap-root slender, with parsnip flavour; leaves widely sheathing at base, irregularly once pinnate, divisions oblong-lanceolate, coarsely toothed and with 1–2 basal side-lobes; flowers yellow; main and small umbels rarely with 1 or 2 bracts; fruits with 5 slender ribs and 4 resin-lines on the outside of each half and only 2 lines within.

2 FOOL'S PARSLEY, *Aethusa cynapium*. Erect annual; stems with nauseous odour when rubbed; leaves glaucous-green, with long ribbed basal sheaths, 2–3 times pinnate, with lanceolate acute lobes; umbels on rather short common stalks, main one without an involucre, small umbels with about 3 linear bracts all on the outer side of the cluster; petals white; fruits with 5 prominent ribs and 5 narrow black resin lines on each half, on the inside only 2 showing.

3 COWBANE, WATER HEMLOCK, *Cicuta virosa*. Poisonous, the roots resembling parsnips; perennial herb up to 4 ft; hollow stems with transverse partitions within the nodes; lower leaves 1–2 ft long, thrice pinnate, leaflets opposite, narrow, sharply toothed; main umbels long-stalked, without bracts, small umbels with about 8 narrow bracts; flowers white, anthers red, then violet pink; fruits orbicular, ribbed with 1 resin line between each rib; ditches; July, August.

4 WATER PARSNIP, *Sium latifolium*. Perennial with creeping root-stock; stems stout, up to 4 ft high, hollow, grooved; lower leaves once pinnate, leaflets opposite, about 4 pairs and an end sometimes trilobed leaflet, all serrate and not hairy; main umbel with an involucre of leafy more or less lobed bracts; small umbels with a few narrow thin bracts; flowers white; fruits broadly elliptic, strongly ribbed, with a thick resin line between each rib; July, August.

1 WILD ANGELICA, *Angelica sylvestris*. Perennial with stout stem **76** up to 5 ft; lower leaves large, twice pinnate, with large leaflets in threes, coarsely toothed; main umbels often 3 together, the

middle mature first, without bracts, small umbels with narrow short bracts; stalks of rays hairy; flowers white; fruits broadly oval, flattened, broadly winged, 3-ribbed on each half with 4 resin lines, the inside with only 2 lines.

2 GARDEN ARCHANGELICA, *Archangelica officinalis*. Lower leaves large, bipinnate, leaflets ovate in outline, sharply toothed, about 3 in. long and 2½ in. wide, hairless; upper stem-leaves becoming very small but with very large sheathing base 2½ in. or more long and lined with many nerves; main umbel without an involucre of bracts, smaller umbels with narrow bracts fringed with hairs; flowers very numerous and crowded in the small umbels, greenish white; fruits elliptic, very thickly ribbed; naturalized on river banks; summer, autumn.

3 MARSH HOG'S FENNEL, MILK PARSLEY, *Peucedanum palustre*. Tall perennial in marshes, late summer, with yellow milky juice, lower leaves 2–3 times pinnate, segments narrow; umbels with several linear bracts with fine points; flowers white; fruits broadly oval, each half with 3 prominent ribs on the back, margins winged.

4 COW PARSNIP, HOGWEED, *Heracleum spondylium*. Coarse growing up to 6 ft; stem hollow, furrowed, bristly hairy; leaves large, pinnate with up to 9 leaflets, these broad and irregularly lobed and toothed; upper leaflets 3 on a very large sheathing base; main umbel without bracts, small umbels with very narrow bracts; petals white; fruits with 5 slender ribs.

77 1 SWEET CICELY, *Myrrhis odorata*. Erect perennial up to 3 ft, strong smelling; stems hollow, closely ribbed; leaves twice pinnate, finely cut and fern-like, softly hairy; leaf-sheath forming a wing on the stalk; flowers white, in compound umbels; no general involucre, but secondary umbels with large pointed whitish bracts; fruits 1–1¼ in. long, shining, ribbed, hairy on the ribs; often near dwellings; spring and early summer.

2 WILD PARSLEY, KECK, *Anthriscus sylvestris*. The first of the Hemlock family to flower in early spring, in hedges and by road-sides often in great profusion; perennial, up to 4 ft; leaves twice pinnate, lobes with acute teeth; primary umbel without a general involucre; small umbels with about 5 or 6 bracts resembling sepals and reflexed in flower; fruits about ⅓ in. long, narrow, not ribbed.

3 HEMLOCK, *Conium maculatum*. Annual or biennial herb up to

5 ft; stems with an unpleasant odour when bruised, hollow and closely ribbed; leaves twice pinnate, leaflets coarsely serrate, hairless; primary umbel with an involucre of reflexed bracts; bracts of small umbels smaller and all to one side; petals white; fruits ovoid, with 5 wavy ribs on each half; damp places; summer.

4 WILD CARROT, *Daucus carota*. Erect annual or biennial, the wild form of the cultivated carrot; in fields and waste places, summer and autumn; stems bristly-hairy; lower leaves twice pinnate, long-stalked; umbels terminal and opposite the leaves; general umbel with 3-forked bracts conspicuous in bud; flowers white; fruits with rows of sharp bristles like the teeth of a comb, tips reflexed.

1 FIELD SCABIOUS, *Knautia arvensis*. Perennial up to 5 ft, clothed **78** with stiff downwardly directed bulbous-based hairs; leaves opposite, connate at the base around the stem, the lower mostly not lobed, but pinnately lobed higher up, all hairy; flowers pale lilac or blue, the outer flowers with larger spreading lobes; stamens 4, long-exserted, with large reddish pollen-grains; flowers all summer.

2 DEVIL'S BIT, *Succisa pratensis*. Perennial up to 2 ft; stem and leaves clothed with long stiff hairs; basal leaves tapered into long stalks, entire; stem-leaves opposite, becoming narrow; flowers blue, collected into globose heads with 2 rows of narrow green bracts; stamens 4, their stalks inflexed in bud; fruits girt by a little hairy cup and crowned by the calyx; summer and autumn.

3 CORNSALAD, LAMB'S LETTUCE, *Valerianella olitoria*. Low much branched annual; leaves opposite, spoon-shaped to narrow, 1-nerved, shortly hairy only on the margins; flowers very small, in clusters, the middle flower soon in fruit; corolla bluish-white, with 5 equal spreading lobes; stamens 3; fruits small and nut-like, ribbed and with a groove on one side, 1-seeded.

4 VALERIAN, *Valeriana officinalis*. Perennial up to 4 ft; basal leaves soon withering, on long deeply grooved stalks, pinnate with about 5 pairs of leaflets and an end leaflet; flowers pale pink or white, in 3-forked loose clusters; calyx above the ovary and inrolled like the fingers of a clenched fist, opening out in fruit like the rays of a parachute, rays with slender side-hairs (plumose).

1 BROAD-LEAVED CAMPANULA, THROATWORT, *Campanula* **79** *latifolia*. In woods in the north, rare in the south, flowering in

summer; stems up to 4 ft; basal leaves on long stalks, ovate-triangular, cordate at the base; stem-leaves becoming sessile upwards, toothed; flowers solitary in the upper leaf-axils, blue or white; fruits at length pendulous, opening by holes at the (actual) base.

2 NETTLE-LEAVED CAMPANULA, *Campanula trachelium*. Very similar to *C. latifolia* (above) but lower leaves very coarsely toothed, and flowers 2–3 together in the upper leaf-axils, only the top ones more or less single; corolla blue-purple or rarely white; fruits pendulous, opening by 3 large holes near the (actual) base; also in woods, from July to September.

3 CREEPING BELL-FLOWER, *Campanula rapunculoides*. Perennial with creeping rootstock, with underground stolons; stems up to 2½ ft, with short deflexed hairs; leaves alternate, broadly lanceolate, base rounded into the broad petiole, serrate; flowers bright blue, pendulous in a slender leafy raceme; bracts linear; fruits pendulous, opening by clefts at the base; doubtfully native in cultivated fields and railway banks; summer.

4 PEACH-LEAVED BELL-FLOWER, *Campanula persicifolia*. Very rare except when escaped from cultivation; among gorse bushes on grassy commons, roadsides and open woods; slender perennial up to 1½ ft, hairless; lower leaves with long stalks and narrowly oblanceolate, slightly crenulate on the margins; flowers few or often solitary, deep blue; calyx-lobes very narrow, becoming reflexed; corolla widely bell-shaped, about 1–1¼ in. long; style-arms 3; fruits erect, opening by pores at the top of the calyx-tube.

80 1 WATER LOBELIA, *Lobelia dortmanna*. Aquatic perennial herb with a bunch of pale yellow thick roots; leaves in a dense basal tuft at the bottom of the water, cylindric and hollow with curved tips; flowers few on a common upright stalk above the water level; corolla pale blue or whitish, 2-lipped, upper lip 2-lobed, lower 3-lobed; west Britain from S. Wales northwards and in Eire.

2 SHEEP'S BIT, *Jasione montana*. Annual or biennial to about 1 ft high; leaves alternate, oblong-lanceolate, loosely covered with long bristly hairs; flowers pale blue, collected into a small rounded head on a long common stalk, with 2–3 rows of broad bracts; corolla deeply divided into 5 narrow parts; filaments of anthers broad and fringed with hairs; fruits opening at the top by 2 valves; June to September, in heathy pastures.

3 CLUSTERED BELL-FLOWER, *Campanula glomerata*. Perennial with creeping rootstock; leaves alternate, lower long-stalked and cordate, upper sessile, ovate-lanceolate, crenulate; flowers in a terminal bunch as well as in upper leaf-axils, blue; fruits opening by pores near the base; summer; in dry pastures.

4 SPREADING CAMPANULA, *Campanula patula*. Erect slender annual up to 2 ft, leaves alternate, lower narrowed to the base, scarcely stalked, distantly crenulate; flowers purplish-blue, in a loose terminal panicle with narrow bracts; fruits soon matured on the lower branches, remaining erect and opening by pores near the top just below the calyx; under hedges and among bushes; summer and autumn.

5 HAREBELL, BLUEBELL, *Campanula rotundifolia*. The specific name *rotundifolia* (rounded leaves) refers to the basal leaves which have often withered and disappeared at the time of flowering during summer and autumn; sometimes called 'Witches Thimbles', the thimbles being the inflated bell-shaped blue corolla; fruits pendulous, opening by holes near the base.

1 YELLOW CHAMOMILE, *Anthemis tinctoria*. End of summer; very 81 like the Corn Marigold but with deeply twice pinnate leaves with acute lobes; flower-heads bright yellow, about $1\frac{1}{2}$ in. diam. on long stalks; bracts in 2–3 rows, hairy; fruits (achenes) smooth, not winged and without a pappus; each flower is in the axil of a narrow pointed bristle-like scale on the receptacle.

2 CORN CHAMOMILE, *Anthemis arvensis*. This is very similar to the next 2 species but is readily distinguished with a lens because each tiny flower in the head has a narrow pointed scale at the base and the fruits (achenes) have rounded smooth ribs; floral axis or receptacle soon becoming cone-like as in the Wild Chamomile.

3 SCENTLESS MATRICARY, *Matricaria inodora*. Annual with numerous barren shoots; leaves 2–3 times cut up into very narrow thread-like segments, hairless; bracts with brown jagged margins; ray-flowers numerous, white; disk-flowers arranged on a convex or ovoid receptacle which does not elongate as in the next species; fruits (achenes) thickly ribbed on one side and with 2 glandular spots like little eyes at the top.

4 WILD CHAMOMILE, *Matricaria chamomilla*. Very like the preceding Scentless Matricary but the bracts with pale (not brown) margins and the receptacle or floral axis is more cone-shaped from

an early stage and elongates in fruit; the fruits (achenes) have no 'eye-spots' at the top and one of the faces has 5 ribs lengthwise.

82 1 THREE-LOBED BUR-MARIGOLD, *Bidens tripartita.* Summer and autumn; annual in marshy places and ditches, spread by waterbirds by means of the 2 barbed pappus-bristles on the fruits (achenes); leaves opposite, deeply divided into 3 main parts; these sharply toothed; heads more or less erect, surrounded by a whorl of leaf-like bracts and an involucre of 2 rows of smaller nearly black bracts.

2 NODDING BUR-MARIGOLD, *Bidens cernua.* Late summer and autumn; lower leaves opposite, upper alternate, not divided but toothed; flower-heads nodding, surrounded by a whorl of 3–6 leaf-like bracts, and an involucre of 2 rows of smaller bracts green streaked with dull brown; fruits (achenes) with 3–4 barbed bristles.

3 YARROW, MILFOIL, *Achillea millefolium.* All summer; perennial in pastures, meadows and waste places; leaves much cut up into fine divisions, rather fern-like; flower-heads usually white but sometimes pink, the ray-flowers usually 5 and resembling an ordinary flower with 5 petals; fruits (achenes) without any pappus, smooth; flower-heads crowded together making a convenient platform for insects.

4 SNEEZEWORT YARROW, *Achillea ptarmica.* The wild single form of Batchelor's Buttons, a favourite garden plant; leaves linear, margined with small sharp teeth like a saw; flower-heads in a loose corymb, each with about 8 white ray-flowers; formerly used in some districts for making tea; often grows with Milfoil and visited by the same insects.

83 1 MUGWORT, *Artemisia vulgaris.* One of the few herbs in the British flora (besides grasses) with anemophilous (wind-pollinated) flowers; rank-growing perennial up to 3 ft, flowering late summer and autumn; leaves deeply pinnately lobed, green above, white with a coat of woolly hairs beneath; flower-heads in a panicle with leafy bracts; flowers very small; crimson, male and female in the same heads.

2 FIELD MUGWORT, *Artemisia campestris.* On sandy and gravelly heaths only in a few eastern counties; August–October; an elegant plant with very slender stems and branches, the latter often

crimson or purplish; lowermost leaves deeply cut into linear segments rather like those of garden Fennel (*Foeniculum*); upper
leaves gradually reduced to simple, linear and bract-like, all hairless; flower-heads very small and numerous, mostly borne to one
side of the branches and nodding; flowers few in each head.

3 WORMWOOD, *Artemisia absinthium*. Perennial strongly aromatic
herb up to 3 ft near the sea, and inland near cultivated ground and
waste places; whole plant densely covered with short greyish-
white silky hairs; flower-heads very small, drooping in a slender
panicle; flowers yellow, about 50 crowded into each head; wind-
pollinated; no nectaries.

4 GOLDILOCKS - ASTER, GOLDILOCKS, *Aster linosyris*. Perennial
herb up to 1 ft high; leaves linear, entire, rather succulent; flower-
heads few, in a close terminal corymb, bright yellow; flowers
about 30 in each head, surrounded by narrow bracts; no ray-
flowers; fruits (achenes) compressed, silky-hairy; limestone cliffs
of south-west England and Wales; August, September.

1 RAYLESS CHAMOMILE, *Matricaria matricarioides*. A low-growing 84
annual and a common weed on roadsides and along pathways,
often among cobbles in farmyards; thrives on being trodden
on; leaves cut up into fine divisions; flower-heads about 3 on each
fleshy shoot; no ray-flowers; disk-flowers numerous on a cone-
like axis; fruits (achenes) very small, marked by streaks of resin.

2 OX-EYE, DOG-DAISY, *Chrysanthemum leucanthemum*. Flowers
with the hay in May and June; perennial; basal leaves spoon-
shaped on long stalks; stem-leaves narrow, eared at the base,
coarsely toothed; flower-heads white, long-stalked; bracts in 4–5
rows with jagged margins but hairless; fruits (achenes) blackish,
with several lighter ribs; no pappus.

3 CORN MARIGOLD, *Chrysanthemum segetum*. A lovely annual
often very common and a troublesome weed in cornfields; leaves
sessile, oblong, coarsely toothed or pinnately lobed, smooth and
rather glaucous; flower-heads as much as 2 in. diam.; bracts in
3–4 rows with broad membranous margins and tops; ray-flowers
golden yellow; fruits (achenes) of ray-flowers narrowly 2-winged;
no pappus.

4 TANSY, *Tanacetum vulgare*. The ray-flowers of this common
perennial herb have disappeared, but the heads of minute yellow
scented flowers are crowded together into a platform making

them more conspicuous to insects; leaves pinnate, the lobes toothed; as many as 300 flowers in some heads; fruits (achenes) ribbed with a rim-like pappus; all parts bitter and avoided by animals.

85 1 GROUNDSEL, *Senecio vulgaris*. Common annual weed, known to everyone, especially gardeners, bird- and rabbit-keepers; leaves sessile and half-clasping the stem, succulent, not hairy; flower-heads few, in terminal and axillary clusters; outer small bracts with black tips; flowers all of one kind, no ray-flowers; fruits (achenes) with ribs lengthwise, not hairy.

2 STICKY GROUNDSEL, *Senecio viscosus*. Very similar to the common Groundsel (above) but sticky all over with short gland-tipped hairs; flower-heads arranged in a loose leafy corymb; bracts of involucre glandular except on the margins; fruits (achenes) strongly ribbed, not hairy; mostly in waste, rather dry places, flowering in summer and autumn.

3 RAGWORT, *Senecio jacobaea*. A very handsome perennial species though a nuisance to the farmer; avoided by stock and often left standing in patches in closely cropped fields; basal leaves forming a rosette the first year, minutely scurfy-hairy; flower-heads bright yellow, often forming a wide flat corymb; look for the smooth (hairless) fruits (achenes) of the ray-flowers and the hairy fruits of the disk-flowers.

4 HEMP AGRIMONY, *Eupatorium cannabinum*. A tall perennial herb growing in patches in damp places by rivers and roadsides, sometimes on moors; stem-leaves opposite, mostly divided into 3 lanceolate acute segments gland-dotted below; flowers crowded into compound clusters, pink, reddish, or nearly white, about 5 flowers in each little head; ripe fruits (achenes) ribbed and glandular.

86 1 COLTSFOOT, *Tussilago arfara*. Almost the first British plant to flower in early spring, frequently very common on railway embankments and in waste ground; perennial with creeping rootstock; flowering stems with small scale-like leaves, the foliage appearing later on separate shoots, orbicular in outline like small rhubarb leaves, white-cobwebby below; rays numerous, golden yellow; leaves formerly used in smoking mixtures.

2 BUTTERBUR, *Petasites hybridus*. Often mistaken for wild rhubarb because of the large orbicular leaves which appear with or just after the racemes of pink to purple flower-heads; flower-heads unisexual, the male and female on separate plants; grows in damp sandy places usually near streams, widely distributed but becoming rare north of the Forth and Clyde.

3 CAT'S-EAR, MOUNTAIN EVERLASTING, *Antennaria dioica*. Densely tufted perennial, up to 9 in. high; leaves crowded, spoon-shaped to narrowly oblanceolate, hairless above, densely covered below with white woolly hairs; heads stalked in a terminal cluster, some male and some female; male pappus-hairs swollen towards the top, those of the female barbellate.

4 WILLOW-LEAVED FLEABANE, *Inula salicina*. Perennial herb with erect stems up to 2 ft; leaves lanceolate, acute, entire or sharply toothed; flower-heads terminal, single or rarely few together, about 1½ in. diam.; involucral bracts narrow, ciliate; ray-flowers numerous, spreading, toothed at the apex; fruits (achenes) hairless; margins of loughs; only in Eire; summer.

1 WOOD or HEATH CUDWEED, *Gnaphalium sylvaticum*. A tufted **87** perennial herb up to 15 in. high; leaves long and narrow, woolly; flower-heads shortly stalked or sessile in the leaf-axils in the upper half or two-thirds of the stem; bracts tinged with brown and shin-ing, hairless outside; a very distinctive species in dry pastures, open places in woods, and on heaths.

2 DWARF CUDWEED, *Gnaphalium supinum*. Dwarf perennial tufted herb, with numerous short leafy barren shoots; leaves linear, covered with cottony hairs; flower-heads in a short terminal spike or raceme; bracts 3–4 rows, woolly up the middle, margins thin and brown; fruits (achenes) shortly hairy; pappus-bristles shortly barbellate; alpine species, only in Scotland; July.

3 MARSH CUDWEED, *Gnaphalium uliginosum*. Summer and autumn; annual, much branched, covered with woolly hairs; leaves linear or slightly spoon-shaped; flower-heads in terminal leafy clusters, sessile; bracts brownish and shining; fruits (achenes) very small, hairless, crowned with a pappus of shining white bristles; in wet sandy places by roadsides, in waste land and on heaths, but shy of limestone.

4 MARSH SENECIO, *Senecio palustris*. Erect annual or biennial; often loosely downy; stem hollow, up to 2 ft high; leaves sessile, lanceolate, pointed, wavy and toothed on the margin; flower-

heads in a dense terminal corymb; involucral bracts in a single row, without smaller ones at the base; ray-flowers about 20, yellow, spreading; fruits (achenes) strongly ribbed; fen districts of eastern England; summer.

88 1 SLENDER CUDWEED, *Filago minima*. Annual herb with slender stem branched at the top, like the linear lanceolate leaves covered with greyish silky hairs; flower-heads very small, in small clusters longer than the leaves at their base; bracts woolly, with glabrous yellow tips; inner fruits (achenes) with a many-rowed pappus, outer fruits without a pappus; sandy places and fields; June–September.

2 GOLDENROD, *Solidago virgaurea*. Summer and autumn; perennial with annual slightly woody stems up to 1½ ft; basal leaves narrowly obovate, coarsely toothed, soon withering; stem-leaves slightly toothed; flower-heads in a narrow oblong leafy panicle; bracts in about 5 rows, with a green midrib; ray-flowers yellow.

3 SEA ASTER, *Aster tripolium*. July–September; found wild only near the sea in low salt marshes, sometimes in large colonies; stems fleshy, with 3 grooves below each leaf, hairless; leaves linear, with a wide midrib and 2 fainter parallel nerves which are continued down the stem; flower-heads either with mauve-blue rays or without rays; disk-flowers yellow; bracts in about 3 rows, green and fleshy.

4 DAISY, *Bellis perennis*. No difficulty in identifying this common but lovely little plant, so pretty but a nuisance in well kept lawns; it ranges right from western Europe to as far east as the Caucasus mts.; the heads close at night and during dull rainy weather for protection of the pollen; it is one of our first spring flowers and may bloom in mild weather even in winter.

89 1 ALPINE SAUSSUREA, *Saussurea alpina*. Only in the mountains of northern Britain and Ireland; perennial herb with unbranched stems; leaves lanceolate, remotely toothed, at first woolly below; flower-heads clustered; bracts about 4 rows, outer short, innermost long with hairy upper part; flowers all tubular, violet purple, smelling of violets or vanilla; fruits (achenes) smooth; pappus feathery.

2 GREATER KNAPWEED, *Centaurea scabiosa*. Perennial; stems hard and ribbed; leaves pinnately lobed; bracts in 8–10 rows, gradually

larger from the outer to the inner, margins black, fringed with bristles like a comb, green up the middle; flowers purplish-crimson; more common in chalky districts; the outer flowers sterile, mimicing the ray-flowers of other members of the Daisy family (*Compositae*).

3 BROWN-RAYED KNAPWEED, *Centaurea jacea*. August–September; a rather rare introduced plant reaching as far north as mid-Perth; perennial; stem and leaves slightly rough (scabrid), the latter oblanceolate, entire or the upper often with a pair of short lobes at the base; flower-heads forming a leafy corymb, with about 6 rows of bracts, these with broad slightly jagged brown tops; a very variable species divided into several varieties; June–September.

4 BLUEBOTTLE, CORNFLOWER, *Centaurea cyanus*. All summer; annual about 2 ft; stems with woolly hairs in upper part; lower leaves toothed or pinnately lobed, woolly with white hairs; bracts in 4–5 rows, chaffy, all shortly cut around the top like a comb; middle flowers bluish-purple, smaller than the outer bright-blue ones; fruits (achenes) smooth; pappus short; often in cornfields and a favourite garden plant.

1 MELANCHOLY THISTLE, *Cirsium helenioides*. A lovely plant 90 mainly in northern Britain; perennial; lower leaves long-stalked, broadly lanceolate, toothed, stem-leaves sometimes fiddle-shaped and with narrow lobes, all covered below with white woolly hairs; heads single or paired; bracts numerous, green and purple; flowers and style mauve; fruits (achenes) smooth, with white feathery pappus; wettish places in pastures and grassy hill slopes.

2 STEMLESS THISTLE, *Cirsium acaule*. Perennial, stemless or nearly so; leaves spreading in a rosette, lobes ending in long sharp prickles, with rope-like hairs on the midrib below; outer flowers spreading and longer than the inner; fruits (achenes) smooth; pappus clothed with long slender hairs; corolla deep mauve or crimson; in dry pastures, sometimes a troublesome weed.

3 CREEPING THISTLE, *Cirsium arvense*. So named because of its creeping rootstock; stems erect, ribbed and prickly like the narrow leaves; flower-heads few in a terminal corymb, of one sex, males on one plant, females on another; flowers rose-purple or rarely white; pappus soon very prominent, feathery; common in cultivated and waste places; fruits (achenes) smooth.

4 SAWWORT, *Serratula tinctoria*. Stiff erect herb each branch ending in a cluster (often 3) of narrow heads about ¾ in. long; lower
leaves deeply pinnately lobed, the upper lobes tending to join up;
stem-leaves becoming less lobed or only serrate upwards; bracts
numerous, margined with short woolly hairs, the uppermost with
coloured tips like the pale purple or white flowers.

91 1 WOOLLY BURDOCK, *Arctium tomentosum*. June–August; leaves
with hollow stalks, broadly ovate-rounded, lowermost often 1 ft
or more broad, rather like those of Rhubarb, thinly woolly below;
flower-heads in terminal flattened panicles, surrounded by
numerous hooked bracts connected by woolly hairs resembling a
spider's web; flowers crimson and purple; rank-growing alien in
waste places; heads attach themselves to animals by the hooked
bracts.

2 LESSER BURDOCK, *Arctium minus*. July–August; resembles the
Woolly Burdock, but flower-heads axillary in the upper leaves
and the hooked bracts of the involucre which are not or only very
slightly connected by cottony hairs; fruits (achenes) angular,
closely warted between the angles; pappus-bristles in several
whorls; rank-growing weed in waste places, rubbish dumps and
by roadsides.

3 CARLINE THISTLE, *Carlina vulgaris*. Biennial often only a few
inches high; leaves very prickly, straw-coloured or yellowish
green; flower-heads single or 2–3, upper leaves gradually merged
into very prickly bracts, the innermost bracts resembling ray-
flowers, pale-straw-coloured; flowers crimson, intermixed with
jagged scales; pappus-bristles fringed with slender hairs; locally
common in chalk and limestone districts.

4 SPINY THISTLE, *Carduus acanthoides*. A very well armed thistle
often around farms and on walls and ballast heaps, by many botanists regarded as a variety of *C. crispus* (see next plate), like that
species the stem continuously winged, but the wings continued to
the flower-heads and not falling short of them; leaves green and
more or less hairless below; heads usually solitary; bracts recurved
at the top and ending in a stiff spine; achenes greenish, 5-angled at
the top; pappus-bristles scabrid.

92 1 WELTED THISTLE, *Carduus crispus*. Late summer and autumn;
biennial; stem erect up to 4 ft, continuously spiny-winged nearly

to the flower-heads, woolly towards the top; basal leaves deeply pinnately lobed and very spinous-toothed, woolly below; flower-heads crowded at the top of the stem; bracts numerous, very narrow, sharply pointed; flowers purplish-crimson, with prominent styles; fruits (achenes) brown, shining; pappus of scabrid silky hairs; June–August.

2 SPEAR THISTLE, *Cirsium lanceolatum*. Biennial up to about 4 ft high; stem winged and armed with long pointed very sharp prickles, woolly-hairy like the lower surface of the leaves; leaves narrow, ending in sharp point; flowers bright purple; fruits (achenes) smooth; pappus feathery; common in fields, pastures, and waste places, a nuisance to the farmer; fruits (achenes) blown by the wind.

3 MARSH THISTLE, *Cirsium palustre*. Stiff-growing annual or biennial up to 4½ ft; stems mostly unbranched, ribbed and armed with very sharp prickles; leaves narrow, pinnately lobed, lobes ending in sharp prickles; flower-heads mostly 3 or more in the axils of leaves; bracts numerous, with sharp tips and woolly margins; flowers purple; fruits (achenes) smooth, crowned by several circles of feather-like bristles.

4 WATER THISTLE, *Cirsium oleraceum*. Distinguished by the usually yellowish-white flowers, rarely somewhat reddish; perennial with slender wingless stems; basal leaves simple or deeply pinnately lobed, upper leaves sessile and clasping the stem, sharply toothed, green, not woolly; flower-heads in a dense terminal cluster over-topped by the yellowish ovate bract-like upper leaves; fruits (achenes) angular; pappus feathery; in moist places by streams and in wet woods.

1 FLEABANE, *Erigeron acris*. August and September; annual or 93 biennial weed; stem more or less crimson; basal leaves narrowly spoon-shaped, hairy, entire, 3-nerved from below the middle; oldest flower-head in the middle of the loose corymb and soon producing fruit; bracts in 3–4 rows, narrow, crimson; outer flowers female and in 2–3 rows, the rays mauve; fruits (achenes) hairy; pappus dingy white in fruit forming a ball nearly 1 in. diam.

2 ONE-HEADED FLEABANE, *Erigeron uniflorum*. A very small perennial alpine plant, rather like a Daisy, known in Britain only on rock ledges in the Inner Hebrides; basal leaves narrowly spoon-shaped, long-stalked, hairless except on the margin; stem-leaves

few, shortly linear, sessile, margined with long slender hairs; ray-flowers numerous, very narrow, whitish, later turning bluish; disk-flowers yellow.

3 GOAT'S BEARD SALSIFY, *Tragopogon pratensis*. Perennial with taproot, up to 2 ft high; juice milky; leaves linear, gradually broadened to the half-clasping base, with a few nerves parallel with the midrib, tips curled; bracts in 2–3 rows, tapered to a point; flowers all ligulate, yellow, toothed at the tips; fruits (achenes) very long, gradually narrowed into a long slender beak, body of fruit with several rows of tubercles.

4 LOW SCORZONERA, *Scorzonera humilis*. One of the rarest plants in Britain so far found only in one southern county, though otherwise widely distributed in Europe; very like Goat's Beard Salsify (above) with a similar feathery pappus but the fruits (achenes) not narrowed into a beak; leaves with 3 prominent parallel nerves and a less prominent marginal nerve.

94 1 DANDELION, *Taraxacum vulgare*. Troublesome weed in fields, lawns and gardens; one of the first spring flowers; full of milk-like sap; lobes of leaves recurved; involucre double, outer reflexed, inner erect; fruits (achenes) at first shortly beaked, at length with a very long beak topped by a spreading pappus of smooth white silky hairs.

2 AUTUMN HAWKBIT, *Leontodon autumnalis*. Summer and autumn; perennial with all the leaves from the root like a Dandelion, deeply pinnately lobed, hairless or nearly so; heads up to 1 in. diam., golden yellow; involucre of bracts tapered at the base into the stalk, with one main whorl of long narrow bracts setose along the middle; fruits (achenes) with minute tubercles; pappus feathery.

3 SPOTTED CAT'S-EAR, *Hypochaeris maculata*. Perennial; leaves in a rosette, obovate-oblanceolate, with wavy toothed margins, usually spotted above with dark purple, hispid; flower-heads usually single on a long leafless peduncle, deep yellow; bracts dark green or almost black, outer ones hispid, inner with woolly margins; achenes shortly beaked, transversely ridged; mostly in chalky pastures; June–August.

4 MOUSE-EAR HAWKWEED, *Hieracium pilosella*. Flowers the whole season; a pretty little species of this large genus; tufts of radical leaves with creeping offshoots; leaves oblanceolate, entire,

74

loosely covered above with long stiff bulbous-based hairs, white-woolly below with star-shaped hairs; flower-heads solitary, lemon-yellow above, often tinged with dull crimson below; fruits (achenes) smooth; flower-head stalks with gland-tipped hairs.

1 UMBELLATE HAWKWEED, *Hieracium umbellatum*. Stem very leafy, umbellately branched at the top; leaves linear to lanceolate, very acute, entire or with few distant teeth; flower-heads pale yellow; bracts numerous, all except the innermost with markedly recurved tips, usually blackish green; fruits (achenes) chestnut-black; widely spread throughout Britain.

2 ORANGE-FLOWERED HAWKWEED, *Hieracium aurantiacum*. 95
Perennial herb up to 2 ft, with mostly basal leaves, loosely clothed with dark coloured bristles and gland-tipped hairs; basal leaves oblanceolate, entire or nearly so; flower-heads few, rich dark orange, the tips of the corollas lobed; fruits (achenes) crimson, 8–10-ribbed; pappus pale; naturalized on railway banks and in open woods; summer.

3 CORN SOWTHISTLE, *Sonchus arvensis*. July and August; a favourite food of rabbits and hares; perennial; stem succulent; leaves oblong with a few short side-lobes, margins sharply prickly-toothed; flower-head stalks clothed with slender gland-tipped hairs; flowers bright yellow, the corolla-tube hairy; fruits (achenes) closely ribbed lengthwise; pappus and bristles white, slightly rough.

4 COMMON SOWTHISTLE, *Sonchus oleraceus*. Spring to autumn; annual weed with thick hollow stem up to 4 ft high, hairless all over except for scattered stalked glands towards the top of the main flower-head stalk; stem-leaves sessile, clasping the stem with often very acute ear-like bases, pinnately lobed with narrow sharp-pointed divisions; fruits (achenes) with slender ribs and covered with short prickles; pappus white, smooth.

1 BLUE SOWTHISTLE, *Mulgedium alpinum*. Perennial herb with 96
erect ribbed stem up to 3 ft, often with stiff gland-tipped hairs; lower leaves pinnately lobed, eared at the base, with a large triangular sharply toothed end-lobe; flower-heads deep blue or mauve, flowers all of one kind; fruits (achenes) contracted at the top, ribbed; rare plant only in mountains of Scotland.

2 WALL LETTUCE, *Lactuca muralis*. An annual or biennial over 2 ft high in shady places, stems very slender, branching at the top into a loose panicle; stem-leaves very much eared at the base, irregularly pinnately lobed in the upper half, green or tinged with crimson; flower-heads very narrow, with few yellow flowers in each; fruits (achenes) hairless, with a short slender beak, closely ribbed lengthwise.

3 NIPPLEWORT, *Lapsana communis*. Annual; stems hollow; lower leaves with a much larger end-lobe and one or two pairs of very small side-lobes; outer bractlets of flower-heads about 6, very small, inner bracts about 8, green, exuding a milky juice when bruised; flowers lemon-yellow; fruits (achenes) closely lined with greenish nerves; late summer until late autumn.

4 CHICORY, *Cichorium intybus*. Perennial herb up to 3 ft, the dried roots roasted and ground and added to ground coffee; basal leaves spreading horizontally, pinnately lobed; stem-leaves sessile, becoming bract-like below the lovely bright blue flower-heads; bracts in 2–3 rows, inner fringed with a few stalked glands; fruits (achenes) crowned by a ring of minute scales, ribbed and marked with transverse lines.

97 1 BLOODY CRANE'S BILL, *Geranium sanguineum*. Perennial; stems 1–2 ft long, very slender; leaves opposite, shortly stalked, rounded in outline, deeply divided into 5 main parts; flowers single in alternate leaf-axils, long-stalked; petals 5, crimson or pink with 5 deeper crimson nerves, fringed with long soft hairs at base; fruits dividing from base into 5 parts which curl upwards and scatter the seeds; shady places.

2 WOOD CRANE'S BILL, *Geranium sylvaticum*. Perennial; leaves opposite, rounded-kidney-shaped in outline, divided into several segments, these coarsely toothed, thinly hairy; flowers in pairs in a terminal leafy corymb; petals blue-purple or rose-coloured, veiny; fruits hairy, dividing as in the Bloody Crane's Bill (above); in meadows and woody places in the hills; summer.

3 SMALL-FLOWERED CRANE'S BILL, *Geranium pusillum*. Annual, softly hairy; leaves opposite, in unequally stalked pairs, rounded in outline, about 1–1½ in. diam., 7-lobed to about or below the middle; flowers in pairs on a slightly glandular stalk in the axils of the shorter leaf-stalks; petals pale pink, only a little longer than the sepals; fruits as above; in waste and cultivated ground; all summer.

4 SHINING CRANE'S BILL, *Geranium lucidum*. Annual, hairless; leaves opposite, in unequally stalked pairs, rounded in outline, 5-lobed to about the middle, averaging 1 in. diam., flowers in pairs on a common stalk in the axils of the shorter leaf-stalks; petals reddish-purple, much longer than sepals; carpels wrinkled in fruit; in stony and waste places and on old walls; spring and summer.

5 HERB ROBERT, *Geranium robertianum*. Much branched annual in shady ditches and hedge-banks; leaves opposite, pinnately divided into 3 main parts, these again deeply divided, sprinkled with a few hairs; flowers few, paired on long axillary peduncles; sepals notched at apex with long slender point; petals reddish-purple to white or pink; fruiting carpels covered with a coarse network; flowers pendulous at night; late spring.

1 STORK'S-BILL, *Erodium cicutarium*. Annual or biennial covered **98** with weak spreading hairs; radical leaves on long stalks, pinnately much divided; stem-leaves markedly unequal-sized in each pair; peduncles long and slender bearing an umbel of few small flowers from a whorl of small bracts; petals purple or pink; fruits very long-beaked; recognized from the Geraniums by only 5 stamens; grassy places; spring, summer.

2 TOUCH-ME-NOT, *Impatiens noli-tangere*. Erect hairless annual up to 2 ft; stem wavy, thick at the nodes; leaves alternate, elliptic to oblong, coarsely toothed, lowermost teeth awl-shaped and glandular; peduncles axillary, 2–3-flowered, these large and golden yellow, spotted with orange or red in the throat; dorsal sepal with a long curved spur; fruits bursting when touched; summer.

3 PURGING FLAX, *Linum catharticum*. A very small delicate annual in meadows, pastures and heaths; leaves opposite, without stipules, very small, pale glaucous-green, 1-nerved; flowers very small, in lax terminal cymes; sepals 5, margin with gland-tipped hairs; petals white, free; stamens 5, united at base; capsule 5-seeded; may be mistaken for member of Pink family (*Caryophyllaceae*); summer.

4 WOOD-SORREL, *Oxalis acetosella*. Perennial with creeping root-stock; leaves all from the root, completely divided into 3 rounded-obovate leaflets notched at the apex, hairy; flowers single on long slender stalks, with 2 bracts half way up; petals white, obovate, notched; stamens 10; fruit a capsule with shining black seeds in each of the 5 compartments; injurious to stock; early spring.

5 MILKWORT, *Polygala vulgaris*. Small perennial with numerous slender branches; leaves alternate, narrow, entire, hairless or nearly so; flowers in slender terminal racemes; sepals 5, the inner 2 much larger than the outer and veiny, resembling petals; petals united with the stamens, bright blue or pink, lowermost crested, stamens united into 2 bundles; fruit rounded, narrowly winged; seeds hairy; all summer.

99 1 WATER FORGET-ME-NOT, *Myosotis palustris*. All summer; perennial with creeping rootstock; leaves sessile, clothed on both surfaces with very short stiff bulbous-based hairs; flowers in a usually 2-forked one-sided inflorescence coiled in the bud stage; calyx shortly 5-toothed (not deeply lobed as in most other species), clothed with adpressed hairs; corolla bright clear blue with a yellow 'eye'; in wet ditches and by streams.

2 WOOD FORGET-ME-NOT, *Myosotis sylvatica*. Perennial herb; stems erect with spreading hairs; lower leaves in a rosette, spathulate-oblanceolate; stem-leaves lanceolate to oblong, sessile, with spreading hairs on both surfaces; cymes one-sided, much elongated after flowering; calyx deeply lobed, with short hooked hairs on the tube; corolla bright blue, with yellow 'eye', rarely white; nutlets dark brown, keeled on one side; damp woods; May, June.

3 FIELD MYOSOTIS, *Myosotis arvensis*. Summer and autumn; annual or biennial; stems up to 1 ft; basal leaves spathulate-obovate, stem-leaves sessile, covered on both surfaces with bulbous-based hairs; flowers in curled one-sided racemes; calyx 5-lobed to below the middle, clothed with prominently hooked hairs; corolla pale blue; nutlets black and shining; on hedge banks and cultivated ground.

4 LUNGWORT, *Pulmonaria officinalis*. Common name given because of supposed resemblance of the spotted leaves to diseased lungs; perennial herb, hairy; basal leaves long-stalked, ovate, up to 6 in. long and 2½ in. broad, mostly with distinct white spots here and there; flowers pink then turning blue, mouth of corolla with 5 rounded hairy scales; introduced and naturalized in woods from gardens nearby.

5 HOUND'S TONGUE, *Cynoglossum officinale*. Early summer; biennial up to 2 ft; stem fleshy, pale green with brownish ribs, villous; leaves linear-lanceolate, sessile, paler below, covered with short soft hairs; flowers in nodding coiled cymes in the leaf-axils;

corolla dull purplish-red, nearly closed at the mouth by 5 humps; fruit of 4 separate depressed nutlets covered with short hooked prickles; flowers with disagreeable mouse-like smell.

1 COMMON ALKANET, *Anchusa officinalis*. Biennial herb up to 2 ft; **100** basal leaves elliptic, stalked; stem-leaves sessile, entire; bracts leafy, ovate-lanceolate; pedicels much shorter than the calyx, the latter divided to the middle; corolla-tube about as long as the calyx, limb blue with a white 'eye'; nutlets strongly wrinkled and covered with raised dots; waste places, probably not native; summer, autumn.

2 BUGLOSS, *Lycopsis arvensis*. Rough spreading annual up to 2 ft, covered all over with bristly bulbous-based hairs; leaves with wavy margins bristly on both surfaces; flowers in simple or branched bracteate clusters; calyx-lobes nearly as long as the corolla, very bristly; corolla pale-blue, 5-lobed, tube curved in the middle; stamens 5, near the base of the tube; nutlets 4, densely warted; June–August.

3 CORN GROMWELL, *Lithospermum arvense*. Spring and summer; cornfields and waste places; strong-growing annual rough and hoary all over with short bulbous-based hairs; leaves narrow, entire, without visible side-nerves; flowers white, in leafy terminal cymes, at first clustered, at length elongating and becoming zig-zag; calyx 5-lobed nearly to the base; corolla without scales in the throat; stamens 5, inserted low down; fruits closely warted.

4 COMFREY, *Symphytum officinale*. Spring and summer; perennial on river banks and wettish places; stems up to 3 ft, of rapid growth, covered with pale bristly rather rough hairs; lower leaves with a winged stalk, upper sessile and continued (decurrent) down the stem; flowers in beautifully coiled cymes at the ends of the shoots, pale yellow, white or reddish purple; nutlets smooth.

5 VIPER'S BUGLOSS, *Echium vulgare*. One of our most spectacular British wild plants, locally common near the sea and in limestone and chalky areas, flowering most of the summer (the drawing hardly does justice to it); up to 3 ft high, with very numerous flowers reddish-purple changing to bright blue; stamens 5, exserted from the corolla; nutlets pointed, wrinkled.

1 BINDWEED, *Convolvulus arvensis*. A beautiful but troublesome **101** perennial with creeping rootstock, often climbing on and strangl-

ing other plants; leaves alternate, ovate to triangular, hastate at the base; flowers usually paired on axillary peduncles, only one of a pair open at once; corolla widely trumpet-shaped, scarcely lobed, pink or nearly white; stamens 5, at base of tube, anthers facing outwards; summer.

2 LARGE-FLOWERED BINDWEED, *Calystegia sepium*. Perennial with long slender stems twining over hedges, bushes and railings; sometimes on telegraph poles; leaves ovate-triangular, deeply heart-shaped at base; flowers single, axillary, the calyx enclosed by 2 large overlapping green bracts; corolla large and pure white or with a pink band up the middle of each lobe; flowers not scented, visited by hawk-moths; June–August.

3 GREATER DODDER, *Cuscuta europaea*. Very slender twining reddish parasite twisting in a counter-clockwise direction; leaves small and scale-like; flowers in dense bracteate heads about ½ in. diam., pinkish-white; stamens hidden in the corolla-tube; style shorter than the ovary; occurs twining on nettles, hops, etc., mostly in southern Britain; August–September.

4 JACOB'S LADDER, *Polemonium caeruleum*. Perennial stems up to 3 ft, with gland-tipped hairs in upper part; leaves alternate, pinnate; leaflets about 10 pairs, narrow, acute; flowers in terminal and axillary cymes; corolla pale blue, but white in bud, or rarely remaining white; tube short, lobes 5, twisted (contorted) in bud; stamens 5, alternate with lobes; anthers contracting into a round mass after opening; summer.

102 1 TEA PLANT, *Lycium chinense*. Slender shrub often growing on old walls, with pendulous sometimes spiny branches; leaves alternate, narrow; flowers 1–3 in the leaf-axils, stalked; calyx 2–3-lobed; corolla deep lilac or pinkish, tubular, with 5 spreading lobes with dark honey-guide markings at the base; stamens 5; filaments with a tuft of hairs towards the base; berries oblong, orange-red; June–August.

2 BITTERSWEET, *Solanum dulcamara*. Perennial, woody at base, with straggling branches several feet long and climbing over hedges or shrubs; leaves alternate, ovate, lower often deeply 3-lobed with 2 small side lobes; flowers in small divaricate cymes, the common stalk opposite the leaf-stalk; corolla blue, marked with violet veins; anthers in a cone around the style, opening by pores; berries globular, red, poisonous; June–August.

3 BLACK NIGHTSHADE, *Solanum nigrum.* Annual or biennial up to
1 ft; leaves alternate, not lobed, or only shortly so; flowers small,
drooping in an umbel-like stalked cluster remote from the leaf-
axils; corolla white; anthers forming a cone around the style,
opening by terminal pores; berries globular, usually black or
green, rarely pale yellow or red; summer and autumn; poisonous.

4 HENBANE, *Hyoscyamus niger.* Annual herb with unpleasant odour,
sticky all over; basal leaves large, coarsely and pinnately lobed;
stem-leaves smaller, sessile, ovate, with 2–3 coarse teeth or pointed
lobes on each margin; flowers all to one side; calyx bell-shaped,
lobes sharply pointed, spine-like in fruit; corolla yellowish, veined
with dark purple, with purple 'eye'; fruit splitting transversely;
seeds poisonous; June–September.

1 GREAT MULLEIN or AARON'S ROD, *Verbascum thapsus.* Erect **103**
biennial up to 4 ft high; stem very stout, covered like the leaves
with soft whitish woolly hairs; radical leaves up to about 1 ft long,
narrowed at base into a short winged petiole; stem leaves smaller,
decurrent; flowers in a thick dense spike; bracts pointed; corolla
yellow, veiny; stamens 5, upper 3 filaments clothed with whitish
or yellowish hairs, lower 2 glabrous or nearly so; on sunny banks
and waste places; June–August.

2 BLACK MULLEIN, *Verbascum nigrum.* Summer and autumn;
biennial; stems simple or branched, up to 4 ft, basal leaves on long
stalks loosely clothed with branched hairs; blade up to 1 ft long and
6 in. broad, coarsely crenate; flowers numerous in a loose terminal
panicle; corolla yellow, with small crimson or chestnut-brown
spots at base of each of the 5 lobes; filaments of the 5 stamens
covered with long crimson gland-tipped hairs.

3 FIGWORT, *Scrophularia nodosa.* Perennial with tuberous rootstock;
stems to 4 ft, square in section, not winged; leaves opposite,
triangular-ovate, doubly dentate; flowers in a loose terminal
panicle made up of little cymes, the oldest flower in the middle of
each; corolla 2-lipped, nearly $\frac{1}{2}$ in. long, green, back of tube and
two back lobes purple; stamens 4; in shady moist places, flowering
in summer.

4 FOXGLOVE, *Digitalis purpurea.* Another significant name is Dead
Man's Bells, for all parts of the plant are poisonous, especially the
seeds; dried leaves used in medicine; usually biennial, flowering in
June–August; basal leaves on long winged stalks, up to 1 ft long,

covered with soft hairs below; flowers mostly towards one side of the axis, drooping, light purple and usually beautifully spotted with crimson, rarely white.

104
1 PURPLE COW-WHEAT, *Melampyrum arvense*. Erect semi-parasitical herb up to 1½ ft; leaves opposite, sessile or nearly so, lanceolate to almost linear, with a few long narrow lobes on each side towards the base, up to 2½ ft long, the upper passing into bracts and pinnately lobed; corolla-tube pink, a bright yellow throat, and purple red lips; cornfields; summer.

2 GREATER BROOMRAPE, *Orobanche major*. Parasite herb growing on roots of Gorse, Broom, *Centaurea*, etc.; stem unbranched up to 2 ft high, glandular-hairy; leaves scale-like, densely overlapping at the base of the stem; no green leaves; flowers crowded in a dense spike, dingy brown; corolla 2-lipped, about 1 in. long, upper lip 2-lobed, lower 3-lobed, lobes toothed and wavy; stamens 4; early summer.

3 MARSH LOUSEWORT, *Pedicularis palustris*. Much-branched annual herb up to 1½ ft; leaves opposite or alternate, deeply pinnately divided; flowers nearly sessile in the axils of the upper leaves, deep purple-red; calyx with 2 broad irregularly toothed lobes; corolla 2-lipped, upper lip hood-like, lower 3-lobed; stamens 4, hidden; anthers attached in the middle; capsule with a hooked lateral tip; all summer, in wet places.

4 LOUSEWORT, *Pedicularis sylvatica*. Prostrate or spreading perennial herb up to 6 in. long; leaves alternate, deeply pinnately divided; flowers pink-red or rarely white; calyx with 5 unequal teeth or short lobes, the longer lobes often toothed; common in Britain, flowering in spring and summer; damp heathy places, avoiding chalky soil.

5 WATER VERONICA, *Veronica anagallis-aquatica*. Perennial herb; stems erect, up to 2 ft high, thick and succulent, hairless; leaves opposite, sessile, lanceolate, toothed; racemes in the axils of both leaves of each pair, densely flowered; corolla pale-blue or nearly white; capsule ovate, swollen, slightly notched; wet ditches, along streams and by the side of ponds; summer.

105
1 COMMON COW-WHEAT, *Melampyrum pratense*. Annual herb, plentiful in woods, parasitic on roots; leaves opposite, sessile, linear-lanceolate, entire but the uppermost among the flowers

pinnately lobulate or toothed near the base; flowers mostly turned to one side, axillary, pale pure yellow; corolla 2-lipped, upper lip hood-like, lower 3-lobed; stamens 4, hidden; ovary not lobed; summer and autumn.

2 WOOD COW-WHEAT, *Melampyrum sylvaticum*. Found only in northern Britain and north-east Ireland; in woods, not common; very similar to *M. pratense*, but flowers smaller (about $\frac{1}{4}$ in. long), deeper yellow, floral leaves not lobulate (entire) and the other leaves much narrower; calyx-teeth conspicuous, the lower ones spreading; flowers in summer.

3 CRESTED MELAMPYRUM, *Melampyrum cristatum*. Semiparasitical herb up to 1 ft high; leaves lanceolate to linear, entire or the upper ones toothed at the base; flowers yellow, variegated with purple, in a dense 4-sided spike; calyx 4-toothed; corolla 2-lipped, lower lip with 3 short lobes, the palate closing the mouth; mostly in eastern England; summer.

4 TOOTHWORT, *Lathraea squamaria*. Perennial, parasitic on roots of hazel, poplar, etc.; no green colouring; stems creamy white or purplish, black when dry; rootstock densely covered with broad overlapping cream-coloured scales; flowers in a dense raceme, nodding; calyx and corolla cream-pink, turning brown with age, corolla 2-lipped; stamens 4, anthers hairy; early spring.

1 ALPINE SPEEDWELL, *Veronica alpina*. Found only in Scotland, on **106**
damp rocks in the mountains; perennial with wiry stems, more or less decumbent; leaves ovate, entire or serrulate, shortly stalked; flowers in dense head-like racemes; sepals elliptic, subacute; corolla dull-blue, nearly twice as long as sepals; stamens 2; capsule obovate, not lobed, about twice as long as sepals, hairless; July–August.

2 SPICATE SPEEDWELL, *Veronica spicata*. Stems erect from a decumbent base; leaves oblanceolate to narrow, slightly crenate mostly towards the middle; flowers in a dense spike-like raceme well above the leaves; corolla with a distinct tube, deep-blue; stamens 2, long-exserted; capsule more or less orbicular, hairy, not lobed, with a long slender style; East Anglia; late summer.

3 EYEBRIGHT, *Euphrasia officinalis*. Erect annual, stems covered with downwardly-directed hairs; leaves opposite, small, sessile, ovate but deeply toothed, teeth ending in a fine point; flowers in axils of upper leaves, some crowded at the top and forming a dense

83

spike; bracts deeply toothed; corolla very variable in colour, white or reddish and streaked with purple, with a yellow spot in throat; seeds ridged; July–August.

4 RED BARTSIA, *Bartsia odontites*. June–September; semiparasitica erect annual up to 1 ft or more; stems bluntly 4-angled, hispid with short downwardly directed hairs; leaves opposite, sessile, lanceolate, toothed, hispid with short bulbous-based hairs; flowers in one-sided spike-like racemes with leafy bracts; corolla purplish-red, 2-lipped, upper lip hood-like and glandular; stamens 4; ovary not lobed; seeds ribbed.

5 ALPINE BARTSIA, *Bartsia alpina*. Perennial herb up to 9 in. high; stem 4-sided, hairy; leaves opposite, sessile, ovate, crenate; flowers in the upper axils of leafy purplish bracts forming a dense head-like raceme; corolla dull-purple, upper lip longer than lower; anthers hairy; capsule twice as long as sepals, hairy; seeds with membranous wings on the back.

6 COMMON CORN RATTLE, *Rhinanthus minor*. Annual; stems slightly hairy on flattened part below the nodes; roots semi-parasitic on those of grasses and other herbs; leaves opposite, sessile, narrowly lanceolate, coarsely toothed, clothed with short stiff hairs; flowers in a dense spike-like raceme with spreading leafy bracts; calyx inflated, nearly orbicular; corolla 2-lipped, yellow, sometimes with a purple spot on the lips; June–August.

107 1 GERMANDER SPEEDWELL, *Veronica chamaedrys*. Small perennial herb; stems hairless except for two opposite rows of long whitish hairs in line with leaves; leaves opposite, ovate, toothed; flowers in slender racemes from upper leaf-axils; corolla sky-blue, fading to mauve, marked with deeper blue lines and with a white 'eye', mouth guarded by bristly hairs on the lower side, 4-lobed; stamens 2, exserted; May–June.

2 FIELD SPEEDWELL, *Veronica agrestis*. Stems weak and more or less procumbent; leaves petiolate, ovate-rounded, serrate; flowers axillary; sepals ovate-oblong, obtuse, faintly veined, margined with gland-tipped hairs; corolla pale-blue with lower lobes white or paler, rarely all white; capsule 2-lobed, lobes with long glandular hairs; usually in cultivated ground, flowering most of year.

3 IVY-LEAVED SPEEDWELL, *Veronica hederifolia*. Summer; slender annual; long side-branches; seed-leaves opposite, persistent, stem-leaves alternate, broadly spade-shaped, coarsely 2-toothed on each

side, 3-nerved from base; flowers solitary, axillary, stalks deflexed in fruit; sepals fringed with stiff white hairs; corolla mauve-blue, shorter than sepals, 4-lobed to middle; stamens 2; capsule enclosed by persistent sepals; seeds grub-like.

4 VERNAL SPEEDWELL, *Veronica verna*. Very small annual; stiff, erect; lowest leaves entire, remainder deeply pinnately lobed; flowers in a dense spike-like raceme; sepals glandular; corolla shorter than the calyx, pale blue; capsule broader than long, deeply bilobed, the lobes projecting between the sepals; only in East Anglia, dry ground; May–June.

5 WALL SPEEDWELL, *Veronica arvensis*. Very small thinly hairy annual; leaves opposite, sessile, ovate, with few teeth, upper bract-like ones becoming entire, thinly hairy; flowers axillary and forming leafy racemes; sepals fringed with short hairs and gland-ular hairs; corolla very much shorter than sepals, dark sky-blue marked by deeper streaks and with whitish tube; capsule rounded, notched, fringed with gland-tipped hairs; April–July.

6 THYME-LEAVED SPEEDWELL, *Veronica serpyllifolia*. Perennial herb up to about 9 in.; stems minutely hairy all around; leaves opposite, shortly stalked, ovate to very broadly elliptic, obscurely crenate, 3-nerved at base, hairless or nearly so; flowers numerous in terminal leafy racemes; sepals slightly hairy; corolla whitish, marked by blue veins, 4-lobed to below the middle; stamens 2; capsule notched, hairy; seeds obovoid, smooth; July–August.

1 YELLOW TOAD FLAX, *Linaria vulgaris*. Perennial herb with **108** creeping rootstock; leaves alternate, linear, entire, 1-nerved; glaucous below; flowers crowded into a leafy raceme with a bunch of young leaves at the top; corolla pale yellow, bulging portion of lower lip bright orange and densely hairy inside; tube produced into a sharp pointed spur; mouth of tube closed; often common by roadsides; July–October.

2 MARSH SPEEDWELL, *Veronica scutellata*. Perennial herb with decumbent glabrous stems rooting at the lower nodes, in marshes and ditches; leaves opposite, sessile, lanceolate to linear, minutely toothed; flowers in slender racemes from alternating leaf-axils; sepals ovate, 3-nerved; corolla pale pinkish-blue or white, deeply 4-lobed; stamens 2; capsule deeply notched; seeds flat, thin, rounded; summer.

3 BROOK-LIME SPEEDWELL, *Veronica beccabunga*. Perennial by brooks and ditches, stems sometimes floating in the water, thick,

succulent and hollow, hairless; leaves opposite, stalked, rounded-elliptic to obovate, slightly toothed, rather fleshy; flowers in slender stalked axillary racemes about twice as long as the leaves; corolla dark sky-blue, 4-lobed; stamens 2; seeds rounded, smooth; summer.

4 COMMON SPEEDWELL, *Veronica officinalis*. Perennial herb rooting at lower nodes, stem thinly pubescent all around; leaves opposite, very shortly stalked, ovate, narrowed at base, distinctly toothed, thinly hairy on both surfaces; flowers in terminal spike-like racemes; sepals lanceolate, hairy; corolla pale blue, marked by darker veins, 4-lobed; stamens 2; capsule notched, shortly pubescent; seeds flattened, yellow; May–July.

109 1 SKULLCAP, *Scutellaria galericulata*. Perennial with creeping rootstock, flowering July to September, 9 in.–1 ft high; edges of square stems covered with minute downwardly directed hairs; leaves opposite, lanceolate, cordate at base, crenate; flowers mostly towards one side of stem, solitary, axillary, only a few out at a time; calyx with a large leafy outgrowth on back; corolla mauve-blue; near water or marshy places in woods.

2 MOTHERWORT, *Leonurus cardiaca*. Nettle-like perennial herb; stems square, often reddish; leaves opposite, stalked, lower digitately 5-lobed, upper 3-lobed, lobes coarsely toothed; flowers in axillary clusters, buds densely villous with long white hairs; bracts sharp-pointed like the 5-calyx-lobes; corolla pale rose, 2-lipped, upper lip erect, lower 3-lobed; a garden escape, flowering June to September.

3 HEDGE STACHYS, *Stachys sylvatica*. Perennial herb with stolons; stem quadrangular, up to 4 ft, hispid; leaves like those of the stinging nettle, stalked, broadly ovate, cordate at base, coarsely toothed, clothed with stiff hairs; flowers in whorls of 6–10; calyx equally 5-lobed; corolla dark reddish-purple, 2-lipped, upper lip hooded, lower 3-lobed; tube with a ring of hairs inside the base; summer.

4 MARSH STACHYS, *Stachys palustris*. Perennial herb; stems clothed on the 4 angles with short reflexed hairs; leaves sessile, oblong-lanceolate, rounded at the base, crenate-serrate, covered with soft short hairs; flowers in a terminal short pyramidal spike, about 3 or 4 in each bract-axil; calyx equally 5-lobed, lobes margined with gland-tipped hairs; corolla mauve-pink, mottled with crimson, 2-lipped; July–August.

1 WILD BASIL, *Clinopodium vulgare*. Perennial with annual stems
up to 2 ft; rootstock creeping; stems square, densely covered with
soft reflexed or spreading hairs; leaves opposite, ovate to triangular-
ovate, loosely and softly hairy; flowers in axillary shortly stalked
clusters; calyx with about 15 ribs and 5 very narrow lobes,
glandular-hairy; corolla purple-red, unequally 4-lobed; stamens 4,
exserted; nutlets smooth.

2 FIELD CALAMINT, *Clinopodium acinos*. Annual in waste places
and amongst crops, up to 9 in.; hairs on stems recurved; leaves
opposite, ovate, hairy on margin and midrib below; flowers about
3 in each leaf-axil; calyx with a flat pouch on the lower side, 10-
ribbed, 2-lipped, upper lip 3-lobed, lower lip with 2 slender
narrow lobes; corolla violet-mauve, white at base of lower lip;
nutlets smooth.

3 GROUND IVY, *Nepeta hederacea*. Perennial with creeping 4-angled
stems rooting at the nodes; lower leaves long-stalked, opposite,
often tinged with dull purple, ovate-rounded, cordate, coarsely
toothed, nerves radiating from base; flowers about 3 in each leaf-
axil; corolla blue, blotched inside the tube with crimson, 2-lipped,
with numerous stiff rod-like hairs across the mouth; early spring
(another name *Nepeta glechoma*).

4 COMMON BUGLE, *Ajuga reptans*. Perennial herb with elongated
runners; stems erect, pubescent with a line of hairs below the leaf-
bases; lower leaves oblanceolate, narrowed to base, margins wavy;
flowers in whorls in the axils of most of the leaves; corolla blue, or
rarely pink or white, marked with brighter-coloured lines.

5 SELF-HEAL, *Prunella vulgaris*. Perennial with creeping rootstock;
stems up to 1 ft, decumbent at base, often tinged with crimson;
leaves opposite, stalked, ovate-lanceolate, thinly clothed with
several-celled hairs; flowers in short terminal spikes; calyx 2-
lipped, upper lip flat and broad, 3-toothed, lower lip deeply
2-lobed; corolla violet-purple; nutlets angular; in fields, etc.;
spring to autumn.

1 CORN MINT, *Mentha arvensis*. Perennial in cultivated fields, damp
paths in woods, and by ponds; stems hairy; leaves more or less
elliptic-obovate, toothed in the upper half, hairy on both sides;
flowers in axillary clusters, the bracteate leaves much exceeding
the flower-clusters; corolla lilac, hairy outside; calyx hairy all
over, teeth short, hardly longer than broad; August–October.

2 WATER MINT, *Mentha aquatica*. Rank-growing perennial herb up to 1½ ft or more, in wet places, rather villous with soft long spreading white hairs; leaves opposite, ovate, rounded at base, largest about 2 in. long, toothed, minutely gland-dotted below; flowers in dense interrupted clusters in the axils of the last 2–3 pairs of leaves; corolla pink, 4-lobed, one lobe notched at apex; July–October.

3 GIPSYWORT, *Lycopus europaeus*. Tall perennial rather like Mint; stems up to 3 ft; leaves nearly sessile, opposite, coarsely toothed or lobulate, the lower pinnately divided near the base almost to the midrib, glandular-pitted below; flowers numerous in dense axillary clusters; corolla bluish-white, dotted with purple, nearly equally 4-lobed; stamens 2; nutlets truncate, with thickened margins; June–September.

4 MARJORAM, *Origanum vulgare*. Strongly aromatic perennial herb; stems up to 2 ft, softly hairy and crimson; leaves opposite, stalked, ovate, slightly toothed, gland-dotted below; flowers in a leafy panicle; bracts ovate, longer than the calyx; calyx equally 5-toothed; corolla dull-purple, nearly equally 4-lobed; stamens 4, exserted; nutlets smooth; a culinary herb; July–September.

5 WILD THYME, *Thymus serpyllum*. Most country children 'Know a bank whereon the Wild Thyme blows', where it flowers in summer, often forming a dense carpet amongst the grass; leaves opposite, spotted with large glands; flowers in whorls in the axils of the upper leaves forming a short dense spike; corolla pink, short, 2-lipped, upper lip cleft, lower lip 3-lobed; nutlets 4, dark brown, smooth; June–August.

112 1 HENBIT, *Lamium amplexicaule*. Low decumbent annual; lower leaves opposite, small and orbicular, on long stalks, floral leaves sessile, deeply toothed; flowers purplish red, few in the upper axils; calyx very softly hairy, teeth short; corolla slender, 2-lipped, about ½ in. long, upper lip hooded, lower with very small lateral teeth; flowering whole season, in cultivated and waste ground.

2 RED DEAD NETTLE, *Lamium purpureum*. Annual or biennial, often a garden weed; stems square; leaves opposite, lower on long stalks, fringed with long weak hairs, widely cordate at base, coarsely reticulate; floral leaves stalked; flowers deep mauve-pink, few in the upper leaf-axils, upper lobe forming a hood, front lobe deeply split and mottled like a spotted orchid; flowers whole season.

3 DEADNETTLE, *Lamium album*. Perennial with creeping rhizome and stolons; stems square; leaves opposite in 2 rows, ovate, crenate-serrate, bulbate-reticulate; flowers white, in axillary clusters; corolla 2-lipped, upper lip hood-like, lower lip broad, split in the middle; whole season often in mild weather in winter or late autumn; leaves like those of nettle, but no stinging hairs.

4 YELLOW ARCHANGEL, *Lamium galeobdolon*. May–June; perennial with somewhat tuberous rootstock and long stolons; stems up to 1½ ft, covered with short deflexed hairs; leaves opposite, shortly stalked, lowermost ovate and slightly heart-shaped at the base, upper ones narrower, coarsely toothed, thinly hairy above; flowers in dense axillary whorls, yellow; corolla 2-lipped, upper lip hood-like, lower 3-lobed and mottled with brown; nutlets very blunt.

5 HEMP NETTLE, *Galeopsis tetrahit*. Summer and autumn; coarse growing annual, up to 2½ ft, stem clothed with very stiff jointed bristly hairs especially below the nodes and with a few gland-tipped hairs; leaves stalked, ovate to ovate-lanceolate, pointed, coarsely toothed, with stiff hairs above; flowers in dense clusters; calyx with 5 long prickle-like lobes; corolla pale-purple or white; stamens 4.

6 LARGE-FLOWERED HEMP-NETTLE, *Galeopsis speciosa*. Coarse-growing annual with nettle-like opposite ovate-elliptic leaves but no stinging hairs; stems with downwardly directed hairs; flowers in clusters with leafy bracts; calyx with 5 long spine-like lobes; corolla 2-lipped, yellow with a violet lower lip; anthers opening by horse-shoe-shaped slits; summer and autumn, often in cultivated ground.

1 WATER PLANTAIN, *Alisma plantago-aquatica*. Aquatic herb erect **113** and growing in the mud at the bottom of the water; rootstock bulb-like with the thickened bases of the leaf-stalks; leaves mostly clear of the water, long-stalked, elliptic-ovate, with a broad flat midrib and 3–4 marked longitudinal nerves from base to apex; flowers in a lax panicle; sepals 3, green; petals 3, pale rose, free; stamens 6; carpels numerous, in a single ring; summer.

2 ARROWHEAD, *Sagittaria sagittifolia*. Aquatic perennial with milky juice; leaves rising above the water on long 3-sided stalks, blade arrow-shaped, the 2 'barbs' almost as long as the point, with 3 main nerves; flowers in distant whorls of 3, upper flowers usually male,

lower female; sepals 3; petals 3, broad and rounded, white with crimson base; stamens about 25; carpels numerous, free; summer, autumn.

3 CANADIAN ELODEA, *Elodea canadensis*. Aquatic; stems submerged in the water, branched and leafy; leaves numerous, opposite or in whorls of 3 or 4, sessile, narrowly oblong, transparent, about $\frac{1}{4}$ in. long; flowers sessile in the axils, in a small 2-lobed spathe; female perianth-tube 2–3 in. long, with 3 or 6 small segments reaching the surface of the water; stamens of the male flowers 3–9; in ponds, canals, etc., often in great abundance; summer and autumn.

4 BROAD-LEAVED PONDWEED, *Potamogeton natans*. Perennial aquatic herb; stems often unbranched; lower submerged leaves linear, gradually passing into broader floating leaves, these broadly elliptic, $2\frac{1}{2}$–$3\frac{1}{2}$ in. long, $1\frac{1}{2}$–$2\frac{1}{2}$ in. broad, several parallel nerves prominent below; stipules often longer than the internodes; peduncles longer than the spike of densely crowded small flowers; sepals 4; stamens 4; summer.

5 PERFOLIATE PONDWEED, *Potamogeton perfoliatum*. Perennial aquatic herb; leaves all submerged, alternate, more or less ovate, obtuse, completely clasping the stem, 1–$1\frac{1}{2}$ in. long, 1 in. broad; stipules very prominent, soon disappearing; flower-spikes $\frac{1}{2}$–$\frac{3}{4}$ in. long; sepals 4; stamens 4; summer.

114 1 FLOWERING RUSH, *Butomus umbellatus*. Aquatic perennial with creeping rootstock, in ditches and still waters, flowering in summer; leaves long, narrow, more or less triangular, lined by slender nerves; flowering stem up to 4 ft, bearing high above the water an umbel of 20–30 pretty pink flowers, surrounded by an involucre of 3 large pointed bracts; perianth of 6 parts; stamens 9; carpels free.

2 SEA ARROWGRASS, *Triglochin maritima*. Tufted herb very similar to the following species and more restricted to coast districts, in salt marshes; leaves several from the base, linear, very fleshy; flowers yellowish-green, numerous in a slender raceme; no bracts; perianth-segments 6, free; stamens 6; ovary superior, 6-locular; stigmas 6, feathery; capsule as in species below.

3 MARSH ARROWGRASS, *Triglochin palustris*. Tufted herb; leaves several from the base, linear, semi-cylindric, rather fleshy, up to 9 in. long, rather grass-like; flowers yellowish-green, numerous

in a slender raceme up to $1\frac{1}{2}$ ft high; no bracts; perianth-segments 6, free; stamens 6, anthers nearly sessile; ovary superior, 3-locular; stigmas 3, feathery; capsule splitting from the base upwards, valves hanging from the top; summer.

4 FROGBIT, *Hydrocharis morsus-ranae.* Floating plant with runners giving clusters of leaves and flowers; leaves long-stalked, orbicular or kidney-shaped, deeply cordate, up to $2\frac{1}{2}$ in. diam.; flowers dioecious, males on a pedunculate spathe, females solitary on a sessile spathe; sepals 3, pale green; petals 3, white; stamens 12–3; female flower similar to male but no stamens; ovary inferior, styles 6, bilobed; fruit fleshy.

5 WATER SOLDIER, *Stratiotes aloides.* Floating herb much resembling a small *Aloe* or the tuft of leaves at the top of a pineapple; leaves in a rosette, narrow, up to 1 ft long, with sharp teeth; flowers usually of one sex, sometimes all male in one locality, sometimes female in another; sepals 3, green; petals 3, white; stamens 12; ovary inferior; stigmas 6; summer.

1 BUR-REED, *Sparganium ramosum.* Erect herb to 2 ft or more on **115** the margins of ponds, etc., flowering in summer; leaves long and linear, sheathing at the base, often much longer than the inflorescences which are branched, each branch bearing up to 12 globular heads of unisexual flowers, female heads below; male heads composed of yellow stamens with minute scales, lower of numerous sessile ovaries.

2 GREAT REEDMACE, CAT'S-TAIL, *Typha latifolia.* Aquatic herb up to 6 ft high; leaves long and narrow, erect, flat, sheathing at the base; flowers in a continuous cylindric spike sometimes over 1 ft long, upper part composed of male flowers with yellow anthers, the lower part female with minute ovaries surrounded by numerous hairs; often in dense masses on margins of pools, etc.; summer.

3 MARSH CALLA, *Calla palustris.* Creeping perennial introduced and naturalized in swamps and near ponds, very local; leaves rounded, broadly cordate, pointed; stalk with a long sheath; flower spike (spadix) terminal, entirely covered with flowers, a little over half as long as the flat spathe; flowers all bisexual; fruit a red berry; June, July.

4 LESSER DUCKWEED, *Lemna minor.* Tiny floating plant without distinct stems or real leaves, consisting of small leaf-like fronds emitting one root from their under-surface; fronds thick, about $\frac{1}{8}$ in. long, ovate to orbicular, often cohering 3 or 4 together; ovary

with a single ovule; on ponds and still water often covering the water; flowers rarely produced, in early summer.

5 IVY-LEAVED DUCKWEED, *Lemna trisulca*. Very similar to the above, but fronds much thinner, oblanceolate, twice as long as broad, minutely toothed at one end, with 2 young fronds growing on opposite sides towards the base; ovary with a single ovule; less common than *L. minor* and also flowering but rarely, in summer.

116 1 ANGULAR SOLOMON'S-SEAL, *Polygonatum officinale*. Perennial up to about 1 ft, with horizontal rootstock; leaves alternate, elliptic, with numerous parallel nerves from base to apex; flowers solitary or rarely 2 in the leaf-axils, yellowish-white with greenish tips, about ¾ in. long, drooping; perianth-lobes 6; stamens 6, inside the tube; filaments hairless; berry small, rounded, dark blue; in woods; spring and early summer.

2 LILY OF THE VALLEY, *Convallaria majalis*. A perennial herb with deliciously scented racemes of nodding white bell-shaped flowers; rootstock slender, base of stems covered by large overlapping acute scales; leaves usually 2, elliptic, about 5–6 in. long and 2½ in. broad, lined with numerous parallel nerves; perianth 6-lobed; stamens 6, anthers large, facing inwards around the white style; berry red, globose; in woods; spring.

3 MAY LILY, *Maianthemum bifolium*. Perennial; rootstock very slender and branched; stem single, scaly at the base; leaves usually 2, rarely 3, alternate, shortly stalked, ovate, deeply cordate at base, 2–2½ in. long, several parallel nerves from base; flowers small in a terminal raceme about 1 in. long; perianth-segments 4, white, spreading; stamens 4; ovary 2-locular; fruit a small red berry; rare; early summer.

4 HERB PARIS, *Paris quadrifolia*. Perennial herb with stem up to 1 ft, at the top a single whorl of usually 4 widely obovate, pointed leaves, with 3–5 main nerves; flowers solitary in the middle of the whorl, stalked; sepals 4, nearly 1 in. long; petals 4, very narrow and more yellow; stamens usually 8; anthers long, with long-produced connective; styles 4, free; fruit globose, bluish-black, ½ in. diam.; in woods; spring, early summer.

117 1 BOG ASPHODEL, *Narthecium ossifragum*. Perennial with short creeping rootstock; stems up to 1 ft; basal leaves in 2 opposite rows, broadly linear, very acute, strongly ribbed with 5 or 6 nerves;

flowers fragrant, in short terminal racemes, bright yellow; perianth-segments 6; stamens 6, filaments with yellow woolly hairs; anthers red; seeds small, with a long tail at each end; bogs and moors, in acid soil; summer.

2 SCOTTISH ASPHODEL, *Tofieldia pusilla*. Small perennial tufted grass-like herb with creeping rootstock; leaves crowded at base of stem, shortly linear, 1–1½ in. long, prominently 3–5-nerved; flowers in short racemes on long common stalk; perianth yellow-green, of 6 free persistent segments; stamens 6; filaments hairless; styles 3, short; seeds oblong, very small, not tailed; northern Britain; summer.

3 YELLOW FLAG, *Iris pseudacorus*. Perennial with thick horizontal rootstock; leaves in 2 rows, linear, pale green; flowers large and bright yellow, 2–3 at the top of each stem, opening one at a time; outer segments broadly obovate, recurved, with a deeper band of colour across the middle, inner segments oblong-lanceolate, erect; stamens 3, hidden below the petal-like stigmas; seeds pale brown-green; wet places and by side of watercourses; summer.

4 SNAKE'S HEAD, *Fritillaria meleagris*. Herb from a bulbous base; bulb-scales few, thick; stems single, bearing a few alternate linear leaves about 4 in. long, closely nerved; flowers single, drooping, widely bell-shaped, composed of 6 free broad segments about 1½ in. long, tesselated like a chequer-board with dull purple, rarely white; stamens 6; anthers ½ in. long, yellow; stigmas 3; capsule 3-valved; moist meadows of some southern counties; spring.

1 YELLOW STAR OF BETHLEHEM, *Gagea lutea*. Perennial herb **118** about 6–9 in. high; bulb ovoid-glose; basal leaf solitary, strap-shaped, longer than the flowering stem, with about 12 parallel nerves; flowering stem with only 2 unequal-sized leaves below the corymb of yellow flowers; perianth-segments 6, free, spreading, 3- or 5-nerved, green below; stamens 6; seeds numerous; in woods, rare; spring.

2 WILD TULIP, *Tulipa sylvestris*. Perennial herb with an underground ovoid-globose bulb 1–1½ in. long; leaves 1–3, strap-shaped, up to ¾ in. broad, with several close parallel nerves; flowers solitary, long-stalked, yellow; filaments of the 6 stamens densely hairy near the base; fruit 1–1½ in. long; late spring, in eastern and southern counties of England.

3 RAMSONS, *Allium ursinum*. Bulb ellipsoid, about 2 in. long; leaves

on long stalks, broadly lanceolate, about 8 in. long and 3 in. broad, contracted at base, with several parallel nerves and oblique secondary veins; flowering stem about 1 ft, leafless, bearing a loose umbel of about 12 white flowers surrounded by bracts; stamens 6; anthers short and ovoid; style rod-like, undivided; seeds rounded transversely pitted; rather offensive odour; spring and early summer.

4 FIELD GARLIC, *Allium oleraceum.* Herb with a bulbous rootstock, the bulb a large white offset at one side of the flowering stem; leaves nearly solid, 8–12 in. long, dull green and glaucous with several rough ribs; flowers in a terminal umbel on a long stalk; bracts 2, ovate and very long-pointed; flowers pale streaked with red or greenish; stamens not exserted; dry grassy places; late summer and autumn.

5 CHIVES, *Allium schoenoprasum.* Bulbs narrow, covered with more or less crimson sheaths; stems up to 15 in.; often growing in dense clumps; leaves usually 1 or 2, sheathing the flowering stem for more than ⅓ its length, rounded in section and hollow, glaucous-green; flowers in a dense umbel enclosed in bud by 2–3 broadly ovate shortly pointed bracts; perianth-segments 6, free, pale purple with deeper midrib; stamens 6; a few maritime counties, rare.

119 1 MILITARY ORCHIS, *Orchis militaris.* Herb up to 2 ft high; tubers 2, ellipsoid; leaves 4–5 in lower part of stem, oblong to oblong-elliptic, 3–5 in. long to 1½ in. broad, numerous parallel nerves; flowers rather numerous in a dense oblong spike; sepals ovate, pink or whitish, forming a hood; lip descending, bright red or violet, spotted, with 2 lateral spreading lobes, apex 2-lobed with a tooth between; spur short; only in southern England; rare; May and June.

2 DWARF ORCHIS, *Orchis ustulata.* Herb up to about 8 in. high; tubers undivided; leaves few, oblong or lanceolate; spikes dense, 1–2 in. long, flowers small, the unexpanded flowers giving a burnt or scorched look; sepals deep purple, converging over the column and the small narrow petals; lip white, with a few purple spots, deeply 3-lobed, the two lateral lobes notched or lobed; spur very short; dry hills; spring and summer.

3 GREEN-WINGED ORCHIS, *Orchis morio.* Herb up to 8 in. high; tubers undivided; leaves few, narrow mostly at the base; spikes loose, 6–8-flowered; bracts thin, pinkish, as long as ovary; sepals purplish, all arching over the much smaller petals and column like

a helmet; lip broadly 3-lobed, pinkish-purple, pale in the middle, with darker spots; spur very blunt, nearly as long as ovary; early summer, in meadows and pastures.

4 EARLY ORCHIS, *Orchis mascula*. Herb 1–1½ ft high; tubers undivided; leaves few, rather broad, often spotted; flowers numerous in a loose spike 3–6 in. long, varying from bright pinkish-purple to even white; bracts coloured, nearly as long as ovary; upper sepals and petals converging over the ovary but lateral sepals spreading or reflexed; lip reflexed on each side, shortly 3-lobed, middle lobe largest and notched; moist woods and meadows; spring and early summer.

5 PYRAMIDAL ORCHID, *Anacamptis pyramidalis*. Tubers 2, ellipsoid; flowering stem up to about 1 ft; leaves narrow, gradually smaller upwards, very acute; flowers slightly fragrant, in a dense pyramidal spike up to 3 in. long, varying from pale pink to purplish red, rarely white, with a slender spur longer than the ovary; lip broad, 3-lobed; fruits ⅝ in. long; mostly limestone districts mid-June to end of July.

1 STRAIGHT-LEAVED ORCHIS, *Orchis strictifolia*. Stem up to 1½ ft high in bogs and marshes, usually hollow; stem-leaves yellowish green, not spotted, more or less erect, oblong-lanceolate, hooded at the apex; spike oblong, densely flowered; flowers mostly salmon-pink or flesh-coloured, now and then reddish purple or white; lip slightly 3-lobed, the sides strongly reflexed, marked with darker dots and lines; spur incurved, ¼–⅓ in. long; May–July.

2 SPOTTED ORCHIS, *Orchis maculata*. Herb often about 1 ft high; tubers rather flat and divided into 2 or 3 finger-like lobes; leaves ovate to narrowly lanceolate, often marked with large dark brownish spots; flower-spike dense, oblong, 2–3 in. long, pink but variable in depth of colour; lower bracts longer than the ovary; sepals all or the two lateral ones spreading, the petals arching over the column; lip orbicular, usually toothed and irregularly 3-lobed, variously spotted or variegated; spur slender; meadows and open woods; spring.

3 FRAGRANT ORCHID, *Gymnadenia conopsea*. Rootstock tuberous, tuber forked; flowering stem up to 1½ ft; leaves few, linear to narrowly lanceolate, upper leaves finely pointed; flower-spike oblong, flowers rosy red or pink, often lilac- or bluish-tinged,

120

sometimes pure white, very fragrant; lip broad, 3-lobed, with a very long slender curved spur at the base; mostly in chalky and limestone districts; summer.

4 LESSER BUTTERFLY ORCHID, *Platanthera bifolia*. Herb up to 1 ft high, with 2 ovoid root-tubers; stem with 2–3 whitish scales at the base; lower leaves mostly 2, up to 3½ in. long and 1½ in. broad, elliptic, upper leaves graded into bracts; spike loose, up to 8 in. long; flowers night-scented, whitish, with a slender spur about ⅓ in. long; lip not lobed; grassy hillsides and open woods, especially chalky soils; June, July.

121 1 BIRD'S NEST ORCHID, *Neottia nidus-avis*. Leafless brown saprophyte in dark places in woods, especially Beech; rootstock a dense mass of worm-like roots; stem up to 1½ ft high, covered towards the base by pale fleshy scales, and clothed with short thick hairs; raceme 3–4 in. long; flowers numerous, dull brown; lip curved downwards, deeply 2-lobed; spring and early summer.

2 CREEPING LADIES TRESSES, *Goodyera repens*. Herb up to 1 ft high; no tubers; stems becoming erect and bearing a few lanceolate broadly stalked leaves 1–1½ in. high and dark green with paler green marblings; transverse veins very distinct; spike one-sided, the flowers in a single row; axis of spike with gland-tipped hairs; flowers white, sweetly scented; lip boat-shaped, with a spout-like tip; northern Britain; late summer.

3 MARSH HELLEBORINE, *Epipactis palustris*. Perennial herb with creeping rootstock, up to 1½ ft high; flowering stem shortly hairy in upper part; leaves several, lower narrowly elliptic, middle ones oblong-lanceolate, gradually becoming leafy bracts as long as flower stalk and ovary combined; flowers often 12–15, soon pendulous; sepals yellowish green; lateral petals white streaked with dull crimson; lip divided into 2 parts, lower half scoop-like, lined with crimson, upper half white with crinkling margins; fens and low places amongst dunes; June to September.

4 TWAYBLADE, *Listera ovata*. Slender herb up to 1½ ft, in shady places in woods, flowering from May until July; stem with 2 or 3 sheathing scale-leaves in the lower part and higher up a pair of nearly opposite very broadly elliptic-rounded spreading green leaves up to 6 in. and 4 in. broad, parallel-nerved; flowers in loose racemes, green, the lip pendulous, deeply 2-lobed.

5 LESSER TWAYBLADE, *Listera cordata*. Very similar to the pre-

ceding but much smaller and more slender, more cordate-based leaves scarcely 1 in. long; flowers very small, in short racemes, the lip linear and shortly 2-lobed, also with 2 very small teeth at the base; on mountain heaths mainly northern Britain; summer.

1 COMMON RUSH, *Juncus effusus*. Perennial with closely matted rootstocks bearing dense tufts of rounded leafless stems 2 3 ft high, clothed at base with rather long brown sheaths and full of soft pith; some stems bearing a bunch of flowers about 6–8 in. below the tip; flowers numerous in close cymes; perianth-segments 6, subequal, sharply pointed; stamens 3; moist places in woods and on heaths; summer.

2 FIELD WOODRUSH, *Luzula campestris*. Perennial herb up to about 1 ft, growing with grasses in rather dry fields, woods and heaths; leaves linear, 1-nerved, the margins fringed with long weak hairs, completely sheathing the stem at the base and with a bunch of long hairs at top of sheath; flowers in heads, the middle cluster shortly stalked or nearly sessile; perianth-segments 6, rich dark brown; stamens 6; spring.

3 HAIRY WOODRUSH, *Luzula pilosa*. Rootstock branched, with creeping offshoots; stems erect, up to 1 ft, in woods and on banks; leaves linear and grass-like, fringed with long white hairs; flowers all separate or rarely in pairs in panicles, the middle one nearly sessile, others on slender stalks; perianth-segments 6, shining brown; spring.

4 SEA SCIRPUS, *Scirpus maritimus*. Perennial with creeping rootstock; stems sharply triangular, up to 5 ft, bearing several long flat pointed leaves often exceeding the stem itself; flower-spikes large, brown, in a sessile cluster or close compact umbel; bracts notched, with a fine point; hypogynous bristles few.

5 BULRUSH, *Scirpus lacustris*. Perennial with creeping rootstock covered with brown closely ribbed scales; stems erect, up to 8 ft high, cylindric at the base and with several narrow pointed leaf-sheaths, towards the top becoming triangular; flower-spikes 3 or more in sessile and stalked clusters; flowers bisexual, with 5–6 hypogynous bristles shorter than the ovate acute jagged bracts and with numerous reflexed barbs; nut obovoid, smooth; in marshes and fens; July, August.

6 COMMON COTTON GRASS, *Eriophorum angustifolium*. Perennial with creeping rootstock covered with strongly nerved sheaths, in acid soil on moors and commons; leaves few, closely ribbed when

dry, hairless; flowering stem up to 1½ ft high, ending in an irregular umbel some with longer stalks than others; spike in flower with conspicuous long anthers; bracts thin and membranous; stamens 3; hypogynous bristles very fine and hair-like, growing out in fruit and resembling cotton; May.

7 RUSTY BOG-RUSH, *Schoenus ferrugineus*. Densely tufted perennial; stems up to 16 in. high; leaves up to ⅓ as long as the stems; inflorescence lax and narrow, about ½ in. long; lower bract with a leaf-like point, about as long as the inflorescence; glumes keeled, smooth on the keel; bristles 6, longer than the 3-sided nut; July; only in Scotland.

123 1 SAND CAREX, *Carex arenaria*. Perennial herb with a creeping rootstock several feet long in maritime sands, rarely inland (Breckland); a useful sand-binder; stems arising singly here and there, up to 1½ ft; lower leaves reduced to sheaths, upper leaves linear, falling short of the spike; spikelets of one sex, at first arranged in a dense spike, lower female, upper male, all narrowly ovoid, about ½ in. long; fruit flattened, ovate, barbellate on the margins; style-branches 2; summer.

2 FINGERED SEDGE, *Carex digitata*. A small tufted perennial herb up to about 8 in. high, stem with several leafless sheaths embracing the base; leaves about as long as the flowering stems, flat, shortly hairy below to nearly hairless; male spike usually few-flowered, overlapped by the upper 1–2 female spikes, the latter about ½ in. long; fruits brown and rather shining; open woods on chalk or limestone; spring.

3 SPRING SEDGE, *Carex caryophyllea*. Creeping perennial herb in dry, especially chalky, grassland; leaves shorter than the stems, rough, nearly flat; ligule ovate; male spike 1, terminal, sometimes with a female flower at the base, about ⅔ in. long; female spikes 1–3, near the males, ½ in. long; glumes brown and shining; fruits hairy; spring.

4 BEAKED CAREX, *Carex rostrata*. Tufted perennial up to 3 ft; leaves longer than the flowering stems, margins finely toothed; spikelets with flowers of one sex only, 2–4 upper entirely male and sessile, remainder female and more or less stalked; terminal spikes about 2 in. long; stamens 3; style-arms 2; nut ellipsoid, smooth, with a rather long beak; bogs and marshes; early summer.

5 BLACK SEDGE, *Carex atrata*. Loosely tufted herb up to 1½ ft;

leaves rather broad, with loose sheaths; spikelets 3 or 4, black or dark brown, about ¾ in. long, drooping when ripe, the terminal one with a few male flowers at the base, or sexes mixed; outer bracts leafy; glumes pointed; style-arms 3; fruits dark and shining, acutely triangular when ripe, beaked; Scottish and Welsh mountains; early summer.

6 CARNATION GRASS, *Carex panicea*. Herb with tufted smooth stems 1–1½ ft, giving off creeping runners; leaves suberect, much shorter than the stems, linear, flat, slightly rough on the margins, glaucous; spikelets usually 3, the terminal male, 1–1½ in. long, the others female, about 1 in. long; glumes ovate, brown with pale margins and a green stripe up the middle; style deeply 3-partite; fruits pale brown, not ribbed; meadows and moist pastures; early summer.

7 COMMON SEDGE, *Carex nigra*. Creeping perennial; stems 3-sided, rough above; leaves linear, longer or shorter than the stems; ligule ovate, acute; male spikes 1–2, terminal, glumes purplish with a paler midrib; female spikes 2–3, close together below the male, 1–2 cm. long, sometimes with a few male flowers at the top; female glumes black, with a pale midrib, nerve ceasing below the apex; fruit suborbicular, green or purplish, very shortly beaked; wet places in acid soils; spring and summer.

8 TUFTED SEDGE, *Carex acuta*. Tufted or shortly creeping perennial up to 3½ ft high; stems sharply 3-angled; leaves bluntly keeled, shorter than the spikes; male spikes 1–3, glumes oblong or obovate, purplish with paler midrib, tip black; female spikes 2–4, curved, up to 3½ in. long, sometimes with a few small flowers at the top; fruit obovate and flattened, beaked; wet places; spring, early summer.

1 MEADOW FOXTAIL, *Alopecurus pratensis*. Tufted perennial up **124** to 4 ft; leaves hairless, finely pointed, finally flat, green, rough to nearly smooth; ligules membranous, blunt; flowers in dense spike-like cylindric panicles, 4½ in. long, ½ in. wide, green or purplish; spikelets 1-flowered; glumes 3-nerved, fringed with fine hairs on the keels; lemma awned, awn longer than the glumes; meadows and old grasslands; April–July.

2 TIMOTHY GRASS, CAT'S-TAIL, *Phleum pratense*. Tufted perennial up to 5 ft high; leaves hairless, narrowed to a fine tip, flat, rough all over or only above and on the margins; ligules

blunt, membranous; flowers in dense spike-like cylindric panicles usually 3–7 in. long, $\frac{1}{4}$–$\frac{1}{2}$ in. wide, green to purplish; glumes 3-nerved, keels fringed with stiff spreading white hairs, shortly awned; grown extensively for grazing and hay; common on roadsides and waste places; June–August.

3 SWEET VERNAL GRASS, *Anthoxanthum odoratum*. An early flowering grass, strongly scented, common in a variety of habitats; tufted perennial up to 3$\frac{1}{2}$ ft high; leaves green, loosely hairy to hairless, rough or smooth, finely pointed, up to 1 ft long and $\frac{1}{8}$ in. wide; ligules blunt, membranous, finely toothed at apex; flowers in spike-like dense to loose green or purplish panicles; spikelets 3-flowered, the lower two barren, the third bisexual; glumes persistent, lower ovate, about half as long as upper, 1-nerved, upper 3-nerved; sterile lemmas awned; April–July.

4 MAT-GRASS, *Nardus stricta*. Densely tufted perennial up to 2 ft high, with numerous vegetative shoots from short rootstocks; culms erect, 1-noded towards the base; leaf-blades bristle-like, very acute, tightly inrolled, hard and stiff, grooved; ligules membranous, blunt, very short; spikes erect, one-sided, green or purplish, axis produced at the top into a bristle; spikelets 1-flowered; glumes persistent, lower very small, upper often absent; lemmas shortly awned; heaths, moors and mountain grasslands; June to August.

5 LYME GRASS, *Elymus arenarius*. A robust bluish-grey perennial up to 6 ft high, on coastal sand-dunes and an effective sand-binder by its creeping rootstocks; leaves bluish-grey, sharply pointed, up to 2 ft long, $\frac{1}{3}$–$\frac{1}{2}$ in. broad, minutely rough above on the nerves, smooth below; ligules short, annular, minutely hairy; spikes stout, compact, 6–12 in. long, $\frac{2}{3}$–1 in. broad; spikelets stalkless, usually paired, 3–6-flowered, glumes persistent, similar, keeled, 3–5-nerved; lemmas densely hairy.

6 COUCH or TWITCH GRASS, *Agropyron repens*. Perennial weed of cultivation, waysides and rough grassland, spreading by creeping wiry rootstocks; culms 3–5-noded; leaves finely pointed, flat, smooth or rough beneath, hairy or not above; ligules very short, membranous; spikes erect, continuous, up to 8 in. long, green or bluish-green; spikelets 3–8-flowered, stalkless; glumes similar, 3–7-nerved, rough on the keels; lemmas not awned except in *var. aristatum*; June to August.

7 PERENNIAL RYE-GRASS, *Lolium perenne*. Tufted perennial up to 3 ft high; culms 2–4-noded; leaves green, hairless, pointed or

blunt, folded when young, up to 8 in. long and $\frac{1}{3}$ in. broad, with small auricles at the base; ligules short, membranous, spikes with a wavy axis, flattened, up to 1 ft long, green or purplish; spikelets stalkless, alternate, spaced, their edges fitting into hollows in the axis; glume 5–7-nerved, smooth; lemmas awnless, 5-nerved; valuable hay and grazing grass; May to August.

1 FIELD BROME, *Bromus arvensis*. Annual up to 3 ft high; culms unbranched, 2–5-noded; leaves green, finely pointed, flat, up to 8 in. long, $\frac{1}{10}$–$\frac{1}{5}$ in. broad, loose hairy and rough; ligules membranous, jagged at the top; panicles more or less erect, open and loose, up to 10 in. long, green or purplish; pedicels slender, up to $1\frac{1}{4}$ in. long; spikelets $\frac{1}{3}$–$\frac{3}{4}$ in. long; glumes persistent, lower 3-nerved, upper 5–7-nerved; lemmas awned; cultivated and waste ground; June to August.

2 SOFT BROME, LOP GRASS, *Bromus mollis*. Annual or biennial, up to $3\frac{1}{2}$ ft high; culms 2–5-noded, shortly hairy at nodes; leaves greyish-green, pointed, up to 8 in. long, softly hairy; ligules toothed, hairy; panicles up to 6 in. long, greyish-green or purplish; spikelets to 1 in. long, 6–12-flowered, softly hairy; glumes persistent; lemmas 7–9 nerved, awned from just below apex; common on roadsides and waste places and in hayfields; May to July.

3 SHEEP'S FESCUE, *Festuca ovina*. Tufted perennial up to 2 ft high; culms 1–2-noded; leaves green or greyish-green, hairless, hair- or bristle-like with a blunt tip and tightly infolded, rough near the tip or all over; ligules scarcely evident; panicles erect, narrow, up to $4\frac{1}{2}$ in. long, green or purplish; axis angular, rough; spikelets 3–9-flowered; glumes persistent, lower 1-nerved, upper 3-nerved; lemmas minutely awned, 5-nerved; heaths, moors, hill and mountain grasslands; May to July.

4 RED or CREEPING FESCUE, *Festuca rubra*. Perennial up to 3 ft high, forming patches; culms 2–3-noded; leaves abruptly pointed or blunt, bristle-like, the basal ones up to 16 in. long, tightly infolded, smooth beneath; panicles erect, loose, up to $7\frac{1}{2}$ in. long, purplish, reddish, or green; branches rough, often paired, unequal; spikelets to $\frac{2}{3}$ in. long, 3–9-flowered; glumes persistent, lower 1-nerved, upper 3-nerved; lemmas tipped with a fine awn; widely spread; May to June.

5 MEADOW FESCUE, *Festuca pratensis*. Tufted perennial up to 4 ft high; culms 2–4-noded; leaves bright green, hairless, tapered to

a fine point, auricled at the base, up to 16 in. long, margins rough; ligules membranous, short; panicles loose, green or purplish, axis rough in upper part, branches often paired, unequal, rough; spikelets 4–8 in. long, 5–14-flowered; glumes persistent, lower 1-nerved, upper 1–3-nerved; lemmas awnless; June to August.

6 CRESTED DOG'S-TAIL, *Cynosurus cristatus*. Tufted perennial up to 2½ ft high; culms 1–3-noded; leaves green, very narrow, up to 5 in. long, roughish towards the fine tip; ligules very blunt, membranous; panicles spike-like, continuous, up to 7 in. long, green or tinged with purple; spikelets in dense clusters, of two kinds, fertile and sterile; fertile 2–5-flowered; glumes narrow, 1-nerved; lemmas shortly awned, 5-nerved; June to August.

126 1 QUAKING GRASS, TOTTER GRASS, *Briza media*. Perennial up to 2½ ft high; culms 2–3-noded; leaves green, hairless, up to 6 in. long, with slender blunt tip, minutely rough on margins; ligules membranous, blunt; panicles with loosely scattered drooping shaking spikelets, these compressed, ¼–⅓ in. long, 4–12-flowered, usually purplish; glumes spreading, persistent, ovate, hooded, 3–5-nerved; lemmas similar to the glumes, cordate at base, awnless; June to August; popular in bouquets of wild flowers.

2 ANNUAL MEADOW GRASS, *Poa annua*. A tufted annual or short-lived perennial; culms 2–4-noded; leaves green, hairless, up to 6 in. long, minutely rough on the margins; ligules conspicuous, membranous; panicles loose, pale to bright green, reddish or purplish; branches spreading; spikelets ovate or oblong, up to ½ in. long, 3–10-flowered; glumes persistent, lower 1-nerved, upper 3-nerved; lemmas 5-nerved, awnless; flowers all the year and very widely spread.

3 MEADOW GRASS, *Poa pratensis*. Perennial up to 3 ft high, forming loose to compact tufts; culms 2–4-noded; leaves green or greyish-green, with abruptly pointed or hooded tip, up to 1 ft long, rough to almost smooth; ligules membranous, entire; panicles up to 8 in. long, purplish, green or greyish; branches mostly clustered, spreading; spikelets ovate to oblong, 2–5-flowered; glumes persistent, lower 1–3-nerved, upper 3-nerved; lemmas 5-nerved, with long fine crinkled hairs at base; important hay and pasture grass; May to early July.

4 WOOD MEADOW GRASS, *Poa nemoralis*. Loosely tufted perennial up to 3 ft high; culms 3–5-noded; leaves pointed, up to 4½ in. long,

minutely rough to nearly smooth; ligules short, membranous; panicles very lax, up to 8 in. long, greenish or purplish; branches clustered, thread-like; spikelets very small, 1–5-flowered; glumes persistent, 3-nerved; lemmas 5-nerved, keel and marginal nerves fringed with fine hairs up to the middle; in woods; June and July.

5 FLOATING SWEET GRASS, *Glyceria fluitans*. Perennial up to 3 ft high in shallow water and wet places; culms few-noded; leaves green or sheaths purple, hairless, up to 9 in. long, folded or flat, rough only on the margins; ligules large and conspicuous, up to ⅔ in. long, membranous; panicles erect or curved, up to 20 in. long; branches often in pairs; spikelets to 1¼ in. long, 8–16-flowered, green or purplish; glumes persistent, 1–3-nerved; lemmas awnless, 7-nerved; end of May to August.

6 PURPLE MOOR GRASS, *Molinia caerulea*. Tufted perennial up to 4 ft high; culms 1-noded towards the base; leaves green, long-tapered to a fine point, up to 18 in. long, margins minutely rough, falling from the sheaths in winter; panicles slender and narrow, to 16 in. long; spikelets to ⅓ in. long, loosely 1–4-flowered; glumes persistent, 1–3-nerved; lemmas 3–5-nerved; wet peaty soils; July to September.

1 COMMON REED, *Phragmites communis*. Robust perennial up to **127** 9 ft high, often covering large areas of swamp and fen and in shallow water of lakes and rivers; culms many-noded; leaves greyish-green, smooth, up to 2 ft long and 1¼ in. broad, closely nerved, ultimately falling from the sheaths; ligule a dense fringe of short hairs; panicles much-branched, to 16 in. long; culms and leaves used for thatching and the panicles for decorative purposes.

2 MOUNTAIN or NODDING MELICK, *Melica nutans*. Perennial up to 2 ft high; culms few-noded; leaves rolled when young, to 8 in. long, flat, bright green, shortly hairy above; ligules very short, membranous; racemes nodding, one-sided, to 6 in. long; pedicels thread-like, tips minutely hairy; spikelets blunt, purplish or reddish-purple, the axis ending in a club-shaped mass of small sterile lemmas; glumes similar, 5-nerved; lemmas awnless; woods and rocky places; May to July.

3 BLUE MOOR GRASS, *Sesleria caerulea*, var. *calcarea*. Tufted perennial up to 18 in. high; culms noded only near the base; leaves equally wide to the abruptly pointed hooded tip, to 8 in. long, hairless except the rough margins; panicles very short and spike-like,

to 1¼ in. long, with short broad scales at base; spikelets 2–3-flowered; glumes persistent, 1-nerved, finely pointed; lemmas 3–5-nerved, toothed at the broad apex; grassland in northern Britain; April to June.

4 TALL or FALSE OAT GRASS, *Arrhenatherum elatius*. Tufted perennial up to 5 ft high, with yellowish roots; culms 3–5-noded; leaves green, up to 16 in. long, finely pointed, hairy above or hairless; ligules membranous; panicles to 1 ft long, green or purplish, shining; branches clustered, rough; pedicels slender; spikelets usually 2-flowered, lower flower usually male; glumes persistent, lower 1-nerved, upper 3-nerved; lower lemma long-awned from the lower third, upper awnless; grassland; June to September.

5 WAVY HAIR GRASS, *Deschampsia flexuosa*. Tufted perennial up to 3 ft high; culms 1–3-noded; leaves green, hairless, bristle-like, to 8 in. long, tightly inrolled, rough towards the tip; panicles loose, up to 6 in. long; main axis rough upwards, branches thread-like, rough, branched; spikelets mostly 2-flowered, purplish to silvery; glumes persistent, lower 1-nerved, upper 1–3-nerved; lemmas 4-nerved, awned from near base; moors and heaths; June, July.

6 TUFTED HAIR GRASS, *Deschampsia caespitosa*. Tufted perennial up to 6 ft high, forming large tussocks; culms 1–3-noded; leaves hairless, green, up to 2 ft long, ribbed above, ribs and margins very rough, smooth below; ligules large and narrow, to ⅔ in. long; panicles very loose, to 20 in. long, green, silvery, golden or purple; branches very slender; spikelets 2-flowered; glumes persistent, lower 1-nerved, upper 3-nerved; lemmas 5-nerved, tip broad and toothed, bearded at base, awned from near base; wet grasslands and moorlands; June to August.

128 1 YORKSHIRE FOG, *Holcus lanatus*. Tufted softly hairy perennial up to 3½ ft high; culms 2–5-noded, downy; leaves greyish-green, softly hairy, to 8 in. long, flat; ligules membranous; panicles whitish, pale green, pinkish or purple, to 8 in. long; spikelets 2-flowered, lower flower bisexual, upper usually male; lower glume 1-nerved, upper 3-nerved; lemmas awnless; common in rough grassland and waste places; May to August.

2 MARRAM GRASS, *Ammophila arenaria*. Perennial up to 4 ft high; culms few-noded; leaves with large overlapping sheaths, tightly inrolled, sharply pointed, to 2 ft long, closely ribbed above, the

ribs minutely hairy, smooth below; ligules large, narrow, to 1¼ in. long; panicles spike-like, dense, to 8 in. long, branches erect; spikelets 1-flowered; glumes persistent, lower 1-nerved, upper 3-nerved; lemma 5-7-nerved, with fine white hairs at the base; coastal dunes; end of June to August; valuable sand-binder.

3 PURPLE SMALL REED, *Calamagrostis canescens*. Perennial up to 4 ft high; culms 3-5-noded; leaves green, very narrow, flat, closely nerved, rough on both sides; ligules membranous, pointed; panicles purplish or greenish, main axis rough; spikelets clustered, stalks very slender; glumes persistent, narrow, 1-nerved; lemma 3-5-nerved, with a short fine awn from the 2-toothed tip, with long fine white hairs from the base; marshes, fens and wet open woodlands; June and July.

4 WOOD SMALL REED or BUSH GRASS, *Calamagrostis epigejos*. Perennial forming tufts or tussocks, up to 6½ ft high; culms 2-3-noded; leaves dull green, hairless, to 2¼ ft long, finely pointed, closely nerved; ligules to ⅔ in. long, membranous, becoming torn; panicles to 1 ft long, purplish, brownish or green; branches very rough; spikelets densely clustered; glumes persistent, finely pointed, 1-nerved, upper 3-nerved, keels rough; lemmas shortly awned, with fine white hairs at base; damp open woods, fens; June, July.

5 COMMON BENT or BROWN TOP, *Agrostis tenuis*. Tufted perennial up to 2¼ ft high, spreading by short rhizomes or stolons; culms 2-5-noded; leaves green, hairless, to 6 in. long, rough or nearly smooth; ligules short, membranous; panicles very loose, to 8 in. long, green or purplish; spikelets 1-flowered; glumes persistent, 1-nerved; lemma 3-5-nerved, blunt, usually awnless; common in grasslands; end of June to August.

6 COCKSFOOT, *Dactylis glomerata*. Tufted perennial up to 4½ ft high; culms 3-5-noded; leaves green or greyish-green, to 18 in. long, at first folded, sharply pointed, rough; ligules large, to ½ in. long, slightly jagged at apex; panicles one-sided, to 1 ft long, green, purplish or yellowish; spikelets in dense one-sided masses, 2-5-flowered; glumes persistent, 1-3-nerved, keel rough; lemmas tipped by a short rigid awn, 5-nerved; common in grasslands; late May to September.

INFLORESCENCES AND
LEAF-NERVATION

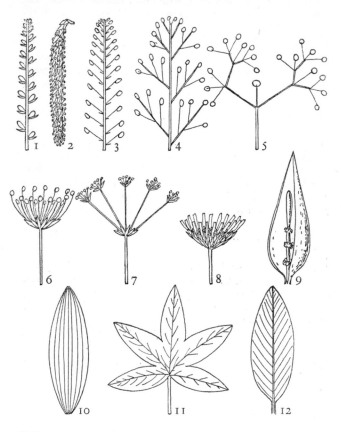

1. Spike	5. Cyme	9. Spadix
2. Catkin	6. Umbel	10. Parallel-nerved
3. Raceme	7. Compound umbel	11. Digitately nerved
4. Panicle	8. Capitulum	12. Pinnately nerved

SHAPES AND TYPES OF LEAVES AND LEAF-MARGINS

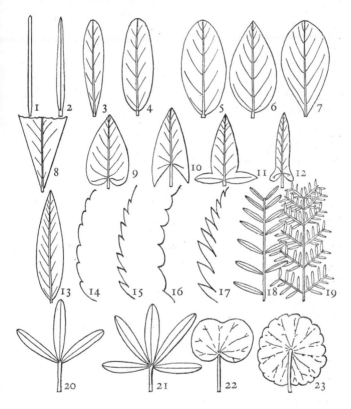

1. Acicular	9. Cordate	17. Pinnately lobed
2. Linear	10. Sagittate	18. Pinnate
3. Oblanceolate	11. Hastate	19. Bipinnate
4. Oblong	12. Auriculate base	20. Trifoliolate
5. Elliptic	13. Lanceolate and entire	21. Digitate
6. Ovate	14. Crenate	22. Reniform
7. Obovate	15. Serrate	23. Orbicular and
8. Cuneate base	16. Dentate	peltate

GLOSSARY OF BOTANICAL TERMS

achene: a small dry seed-like fruit

acicular: shaped like a needle

acuminate: gradually pointed

alien: introduced (not native)

alternate: not opposite

anemophilous: wind-borne

annual: lasting only one year or season

anther: terminal portion of stamen bearing the pollen

aquatic: living in, or partly in, water

auriculate: eared

awned: provided with a slender bristle-like projection

axillary: in the axil of a leaf or bract

barbellate: barbed

berry: juicy fruit with seeds immersed in pulp

biennial: lasting two years or two seasons

bipinnate: twice pinnate (see pinnate)

bisexual: with male and female parts in the same flower

bract: modified leaf at base of flower stalk or leaves around a flower-head

bracteole: small bract on the flower-stalk

calyx: outermost, usually green, floral envelope

capitulum: a head of flowers (as in the daisy)

capsule: dry fruit which opens and releases the seeds

carpel: one or more divisions of ovary or fruit

catkin: slender, often pendulous spike of flowers

connate: united similar parts

cordate: heart-shaped

corolla: collective name for the petals

corymb: more or less flat-topped assemblage of flowers

crenate: with blunt curved teeth

crenulate: diminutive of crenate

culm: stem of grasses

cuneate: wedge-shaped

cyme: an inflorescence repeatedly divided with the oldest flower in the middle of each fork

deciduous: falling off

deltoid: triangular

dentate: toothed on the margin

digitate: applied to leaves divided like the fingers of the hand

dioecious: male and female flowers on different plants

disk-flower: flowers in the middle of a head with rays

drupe: stone-fruit such as a plum

ellipsoid: elliptic in outline

elliptic: shaped like an ellipse

entire: neither toothed nor lobed

female: the fruiting part of a flower

filament: stalk of a stamen

fruit: the fertilized and mature ovary or carpel

glabrous: not hairy

glaucous: with a whitish-blue lustre like the bloom of a grape

globose: round like a globe

glume: two empty bracts at base of grass-spikelet

hastate: like sagittate, but lobes spreading at a right angle

inferior: below

inflorescence: collection of flowers on a shoot

involucre: a ring of bracts surrounding one or more flowers *lanceolate:* lance-shaped

leaflet: unit of a compound leaf

lemma: lower bract enclosing grass flower

ligule: outgrowth at top of grass leaf-sheath

limb: blade of leaf or petal

linear: long and very narrow

locular: divided into chambers

loculus: a chamber or cavity of an ovary, fruit or anther

longitudinal: lengthwise

male: a plant or flower which bears stamens

monoecious: male and female flowers on the same plant

nectary: organ in which nectar is secreted

node: point of insertion of a leaf or leaves

nutlet: little nut

oblanceolate: reverse of lanceolate

oblong: about twice as long as broad with more or less straight sides

obovate: reverse of ovate

opposite: inserted at same level, as leaves on a shoot

orbicular: circular

ovary: female part of the flower, represented by the carpels

ovate: egg-shaped

ovoid: ovate in outline

ovule: the organ which after fertilization develops into a seed

panicle: a branched raceme

pappus: modified calyx of the *Compositae*

pedicel: ultimate flower-stalk

pedicellate: stalked

peduncle: common stalk of more than one flower

peltate: attached in the middle (like the stalk of a mushroom)

perennial: lasting more than two years

petal: the usually coloured inner part of the floral leaves

petiolate: stalked leaves

petiole: leaf-stalk

pinnate: divided like a feather

plumose: feather-like

pollen: the dust-like contents of an anther

pubescent: hairy

raceme: unbranched inflorescence with individual flowers stalked

radical: from the root

ray-flower: marginal flower of the *Compositae*

receptacle: floral axis

regular: symmetrical

reniform: kidney-shaped

reticulate: like a net

rootstock: underground stem

sagittate: like an arrow

scabrid: rough

semiaquatic: partly in the water

sepal: outer often green part of flower

serrate: with saw-like teeth

serrulate: diminutive of serrate

sessile: stalkless

spadix: spike with a fleshy axis (as in *Arum*)

spathe: large bract around a spadix

spike: stiff unbranched inflorescence with flowers not stalked

spikelet: unit of grass flower-head

stamen: the male organ of a flower

stellate: star-like

sterile: barren

stigma: tip or tips of the style

stipule: appendage at base of leaf or leaf-stalk

stolon: basal branch which roots

style: narrow portion of pistil between ovary and stigma

superior: placed above

ternate: in threes

tomentose: densely covered with short hairs

trifoliolate: with three leaflets (as in Clover)

triternate: thrice divided

umbel: inflorescence branched like the ribs of an umbrella

unisexual: of one sex

valve: portion into which a fruit or other organ separates or opens

viscid: sticky

whorl: arranged in a circle around an axis

INDEX TO COMMON NAMES
INDEX TO BOTANICAL NAMES
INDEX TO FAMILIES

INDEX TO COMMON NAMES

INDEX TO BOTANICAL NAMES

Lycopus europaeus 111: 3
Lysimachia nummularia 66: 2
Lysimachia thyrsiflora 66: 3
Lysimachia vulgaris 66: 1
Lythrum salicaria 70: 4

Maianthemum bifolium 116: 3
Malus pumila 3: 1
Malva neglecta 29: 4
Malva sylvestris 29: 3
Matricaria chamomilla 81: 4
Matricaria inodora 81: 3
Matricaria matricarioides 84: 1
Medicago falcata 14: 3
Medicago lupulina 14: 4
Medicago sativa 14: 2
Melampyrum arvense 104: 1
Melampyrum cristatum 105: 3
Melampyrum pratense 105: 1
Melampyrum sylvaticum 105: 2
Melica nutans 127: 2
Melilotus altissima 14: 1
Mentha aquatica 111: 2
Mentha arvensis 111: 1
Menyanthes trifoliata 62: 5
Mercurialis perennis 27: 2
Molinia caerulea 126: 6
Moneses uniflora 40: 4
Monotropa hypopitys 39: 3
Mulgedium alpinum 96: 1
Myosotis arvensis 99: 3
Myosotis palustris 99: 1
Myosotis sylvatica 99: 2
Myosurus minimus 49: 3
Myrica gale 23: 2
Myrrhis odorata 77: 1

Nardus stricta 124: 4
Narthecium ossifragum 117: 1
Neottia nidus-avis 121: 1
Nepeta hederacea 110: 3
Nuphar lutea 53: 2
Nymphaea alba 53: 1

Ononis repens 17: 1
Orchis maculata 120: 2
Orchis mascula 119: 4
Orchis militaris 119: 1
Orchis morio 119: 3
Orchis strictifolia 120: 1
Orchis ustulata 119: 2
Origanum vulgare 111: 4

Orobanche major 104: 2
Oxalis acetosella 98: 4
Oxycoccus palustris 41: 4
Oxyria digyna 68: 5
Oxytropis campestris 13: 3

Padus racemosa 4: 2
Papaver argemone 54: 3
Papaver dubium 54: 2
Papaver rhoeas 54: 1
Paris quadrifolia 116: 4
Parnassia palustris 73: 5
Pastinaca sativa 75: 1
Pedicularis palustris 104: 3
Pedicularis sylvatica 104: 4
Petasites hybridus 86: 2
Peucedanum palustre 76: 3
Phleum pratense 124: 2
Phragmites communis 127: 1
Phyllodoce caerulea 37: 4
Picea abies 1: 2
Pinguicula vulgaris 63: 1
Pimpinella saxifraga 74: 1
Pinus sylvestris 1: 1
Plantago coronopus 65: 5
Plantago lanceolata 65: 3
Plantago major 65: 1
Plantago maritima 65: 4
Plantago media 65: 2
Platanthera bifolia 120: 4
Poa annua 126: 2
Poa nemoralis 126: 4
Poa pratensis 126: 3
Polemonium caeruleum 101: 4
Polygala vulgaris 98: 5
Polygonatum officinale 116: 1
Polygonum amphibium 67: 2
Polygonum aviculare 67: 6
Polygonum convolvulus 67: 5
Polygonum hydropiper 67: 4
Polygonum persicaria 67: 3
Polygonum viviparum 67: 1
Populus tremula 23: 3
Potamogeton natans 113: 4
Potamogeton perfoliatum 113: 5
Potentilla anserina 8: 2
Potentilla argentea 7: 2
Potentilla erecta 7: 4
Potentilla fruticosa 7: 1
Potentilla palustris 8: 3
Potentilla reptans 8: 1
Potentilla sibbaldii 6: 4

Potentilla verna 7: 3
Primula farinosa 63: 4
Primula veris 63: 3
Prunella vulgaris 110: 5
Prunus avium 4: 1
Prunus spinosa 3: 3
Pulmonaria officinalis 99: 4
Pyrola minor 40: 2
Pyrola rotundifolia 40: 1
Pyrola secunda 40: 3

Quercus robur 26: 2

Ranunculus acris 48: 2
Ranunculus aquatilis 49: 2
Ranunculus arvensis 49: 1
Ranunculus auricomus 48: 3
Ranunculus bulbosus 47: 4
Ranunculus flammula 47: 3
Ranunculus hederaceus 50: 5
Ranunculus lingua 47: 2
Ranunculus repens 48: 1
Ranunculus sceleratus 48: 4
Raphanus raphanistrum 36: 3
Rhamnus catharticus 19: 4
Rhinanthus minor 106: 6
Rhododendron ponticum 39: 1
Ribes alpinum 11: 2
Rorippa islandica 34: 4
Rosa canina 10: 3
Rubus arcticus 9: 3
Rubus caesius 9: 4
Rubus chamaemorus 9: 2
Rubus fruticosus 10: 2
Rubus idaeus 10: 1
Rubus saxatilis 9: 1
Rumex acetosa 68: 2
Rumex acetosella 68: 1
Rumex crispus 68: 4
Rumex longifolius 68: 3

Sagina nodosa 60: 1
Sagina procumbens 60: 2
Sagittaria sagittifolia 113: 2
Salicornia herbacea 61: 5
Salix caprea 20: 4
Salix fragilis 20: 2
Salix herbacea 21: 3
Salix lanata 21: 1
Salix pentandra 20: 1
Salix repens 21: 2
Salix reticulata 21: 4
Salix viminalis 20: 3

Sambucus nigra 45: 1
Sambucus racemosa 45: 2
Sanicula europaea 74: 4
Saussurea alpina 89: 1
Saxifraga aizoides 72: 4
Saxifraga cernua 72: 5
Saxifraga granulata 73: 3
Saxifraga hirculus 73: 1
Saxifraga nivalis 72: 2
Saxifraga oppositifolia 72: 3
Saxifraga stellaris 72: 1
Saxifraga tridactylites 73: 2
Schoenus ferrugineus 122: 7
Scirpus lacustris 122: 5
Scirpus maritimus 122: 4
Scleranthus annuus 60: 6
Scorzonera humilis 93: 4
Scrophularia nodosa 103: 3
Scutellaria galericulata 109: 1
Senecio jacobaea 85: 3
Senecio palustris 87: 4
Senecio viscosus 85: 2
Senecio vulgaris 85: 1
Sedum acre 71: 4
Sedum album 71: 5
Sedum roseum 71: 1
Sedum spurium 71: 3
Sedum telephium 71: 2
Serratula tinctoria 90: 4
Sesleria caerulea var. calcarea 127: 3
Sherardia arvensis 43: 4
Silene acaulis 55: 4
Silene cucubalus 55: 1
Silene nutans 55: 2
Silene otites 55: 3
Sinapis arvensis 36: 2
Sisymbrium officinale 35: 1
Sisymbrium sophia 35: 2
Sium latifolium 75: 4
Solanum dulcamara 102: 2
Solanum nigrum 102: 3
Solidago virgaurea 88: 2
Sonchus arvensis 95: 3
Sonchus oleraceus 95: 4
Sorbus aucuparia 2: 2
Sorbus intermedia 2: 1
Sparganium ramosum 115: 1
Spergula arvensis 60: 3
Spergularia rubra 60: 4
Stachys palustris 109: 4
Stachys sylvatica 109: 3
Stellaria graminea 58: 4

Stellaria holostea 58: 3
Stellaria media 58: 2
Stellaria nemorum 58: 1
Stratiotes aloides 114: 5
Succisa pratensis 78: 2
Symphytum officinale 100: 4

Tanacetum vulgare 84: 4
Taraxacum vulgare 94: 1
Taxus baccata 1: 4
Thalictrum alpinum 51: 3
Thalictrum flavum 51: 1
Thlaspi alpestre 32: 4
Thlaspi arvense 32: 3
Thymus serpyllum 111: 5
Tilia cordata 11: 1
Tofieldia pusilla 117: 2
Tragopogon pratensis 93: 3
Trifolium arvense 15: 4
Trifolium aureum 15: 1
Trifolium fragiferum 15: 3
Trifolium hybridum 16: 3
Trifolium medium 16: 4
Trifolium pratense 16: 1
Trifolium procumbens 14: 5
Trifolium repens 16: 2
Trientalis europaea 64: 2
Triglochin maritima 114: 2
Triglochin palustris 114: 3
Trollius europaeus 52: 1
Tulipa sylvestris 118: 2
Turritis glabra 33: 4
Tussilago farfara 86: 1
Typha latifolia 115: 2

Ulmus glabra 24: 1
Urtica dioica 27: 3
Urtica urens 27: 4
Utricularia vulgaris 63: 2

Vaccinium myrtillus 41: 1
Vaccinium uliginosum 41: 2
Vaccinium vitis-idaea 41: 3
Valeriana officinalis 78: 4
Valerianella olitoria 78: 3
Verbascum nigrum 103: 2
Verbascum thapsus 103: 1
Veronica agrestis 107: 2
Veronica alpina 106: 1
Veronica anagallis-aquatica 104: 5
Veronica arvensis 107: 5
Veronica beccabunga 108: 3
Veronica chamaedrys 107: 1
Veronica hederifolia 107: 3
Veronica officinalis 108: 4
Veronica scutellata 108: 2
Veronica serpyllifolia 107: 6
Veronica spicata 106: 2
Veronica verna 107: 4
Viburnum opulus 45: 3
Vicia cracca 12: 4
Vicia sepium 12: 5
Vinca minor 43: 5
Viola arvensis 31: 5
Viola canina 30: 4
Viola hirta 30: 2
Viola odorata 30: 1
Viola palustris 28: 2
Viola riviniana 30: 3
Viola tricolor 31: 4

INDEX TO FAMILIES